W9-DJN-554

Dear Charles

THE MACMILLAN COMPANY
NEW YORK • CHICAGO
DALLAS • ATLANTA • SAN FRANCISCO
LONDON • MANILA
BRETT-MACMILLAN LTD.
TORONTO

Dear Charles

Letters to a Young Minister

BY WESLEY SHRADER

NEW YORK *The Macmillan Company* 1958

PRINTED IN THE UNITED STATES OF AMERICA

Third Printing, 1958

To Agnes

INTRODUCTION

Several years ago the widow of a dear friend of mine notified me that I was to be given her husband's large library. Though such a bequest was not in the deceased man's will, his wife assured me that he had spoken to her on several occasions concerning the disposal of his many books, and that I was to be the chief benefactor.

This pleased me no little, for Charles, in recent years, had held some of the largest and most prominent churches in the entire country. Naturally his salary had been much greater than that of the average minister. Thus it was possible with such an income for him to invest in books far beyond the reach of most men.

I well remember my last visit with Charles, a short time after he had become pastor of the largest church in Mammonville, a city of more than 300,000 population. I was interviewed (given the third degree would be more accurate) by an efficient, spinsterish type of person whom I took to be one of the secretaries on the staff. After presenting my credentials, which consisted of nothing more than "being a friend of long standing," I was told that I could see Dr. Prince for not longer than fifteen minutes.

He was sitting czar-like behind an imposing desk. The correctly fitted pince-nez glasses gave him a distinguished appearance that made me feel uncomfortable in spite of the familiarity I felt toward him. My awkwardness soon vanished, for Charles, at this stage of his development, was more gracious, attractive, and utterly charming than ever before. As I was ushered in, he flashed an ingratiating smile, and I was completely at ease. His luxuriant growth of brown wavy hair was perfectly groomed, as was every detail of his clothes and person.

Charles laid aside a little book that he had been studying. (I was curious to know how men spend their time in such an impressive atmosphere. The title of the book was *Denominational Distinctives.* Since it is one of the books in the bequest, I will have the opportunity of studying it, as Charles did.) With a warmth that melted all my reserve, he extended his huge hand and shouted: "Wesley, my boy, sit down and tell me all about yourself. How have you been getting along? Doggone it, we haven't seen each other for too long a time. Why in heaven's name don't you bring the wife and children around to see us? You don't have to wait for an invitation. Drop in any time. Any time will suit us."

I started to answer, but before I could think of the right thing to say he continued: "By the way, how is the little woman, and the children? You know, Wesley, the Lord has been good to you. Priscilla and I have never had any children; it apparently was not the Lord's will. You have been the lucky one. Of all the men in our class, I envy you more than any. You have been sensible enough to stay with smaller churches where the strain is not so great; you have a splendid family, and so help me, you look in the best of health. How do you keep your weight down?"

After several minutes of this, I glanced at the clock and noticed that the fifteen-minute period was just about up, and suggested that I ought to be going. "Nothing doing!" Charles expostulated. "That fifteen-minute rule is for salesmen, cranks, and so on. I've got to have at least thirty minutes with my friends, for old time's sake."

During the remaining time I did not hear much of what Charles was saying; I was literally fascinated by the multiple volumes which covered the four walls of the study. There were books of every kind and classification—theology, philosophy, sociology, biology, natural science, history, the English classics, sacred scriptures from all religions. There were the technical books such as Bible commentaries, the Greek and Hebrew lexicons. There was one entire shelf devoted to "rare" books; these were irreplaceable. In addition, there were several shelves of the well known best sellers, fiction and non-fiction.

When the second fifteen-minute period was up, Charles, in the smoothest possible manner, signaled that the tête-à-tête was over. He did so by shoving his roller chair back a little, thus giving the appearance of being ready to rise. I beat him to it, however, and excused myself. In parting, we assured each other that it was good to renew acquaintances and that we would get our families together for a sociable evening in the near future.

I doubt that this "sociable evening" would ever have taken place. For one thing Charles had an engagement, of some kind, every night in the week. But it was nice to consider the possibility of reestablishing an old friendship.

However, within a few weeks, Charles, at the age of forty-two, died unexpectedly. Thus our denomination lost one of its choicest men, a real leader, one who will be hard to replace.

As I read the beautiful tributes to Charles which appeared in all of our denominational papers, I found myself repeatedly asking the questions: "What was the secret of his amazing success? How did he do it? How did he completely win the hearts of his brethren? How did he get to the top so quickly?"

Though I would never have dared suggest such a thing to any of our associates, Charles was not a good preacher. The reason why I kept silent is obvious. He and I had been classmates; he had got to the top; he had received, at an early age, every honor the denomination could bestow on a man. And he had outstripped the rest of us. To mention the possibility that he was a weak preacher would result in my being labeled "cheap" and "envious."

It is true that Charles had developed a theatrical manner, and in the pulpit he could tell a story (use an illustration) with masterful skill. It is also true that he knew how "to give an invitation." For readers who may not be informed about such things, the number of additions (joiners) that a pastor has during his ministry is the most generally accepted standard of success now employed by several denominations. Getting people to come down the aisle, preferably in tears, is an indication that the Holy Spirit has been at work. According to a well known viewpoint, the Holy Spirit works better for some preachers than for others. The ability of getting the Holy Spirit to work in the hearts of the people to the point of causing them to "make a public profession of faith" seems to be dependent on three things: the preacher's prayer life (which no one has any way of checking on), his ability to use an illustration, and his skill in giving the invitation.

But I still insist, in spite of these accomplishments and even though he has greatly befriended me, that Charles was not a good preacher. For one thing, several of his more intimate friends, including myself, knew, beyond a doubt, that although his library was exceedingly large, he never read. His chief reading consisted of denominational literature and sermon books. The "sermon books" were the only ones which Charles did not display in his study. He kept these in his private den at the parsonage. On Saturday evening he frantically skimmed through them until "he got an idea" and took down a few notes for his morning and evening sermons.

The only poor stroke of strategy that Charles Prince ever made was early in his ministry when he accepted the tedious job of writing a year's Sunday-school lessons for the Board. When a man writes, he puts what he knows on paper where all can see. Faking a sermon from the pulpit is one thing; faking a written article is quite another, and not even Charles could get by with that! Those lessons were as thin and bare as Charles's soul.

One of our intellectual friends, a fellow who had gained quite a reputation for being jealous of Charles, had a comment to make concerning the Sunday-school lessons. He said that they reminded him of a man whose wife called to him upstairs that guests had arrived and were waiting for him in the living room. The man rushed madly downstairs to greet his friends, but he had failed to put on his clothes. He was stark naked, without a stitch. What made the situation more pathetic was that no one laughed and no one hinted of his condition, not even his wife. The poor fellow was completely unaware that he had presented his nakedness for all to see.

Charles may have been like that, but in some ways I have doubted it, for the very good reason that he never again put anything in print. I am sure he suspected his condition.

My questions still persisted. "What was the secret of his

amazing success? How did he get so smooth, so confident, so polished?"

The answer was not long delayed following the delivery of Charles's library to my own quarters. For weeks I did nothing but finger and fondle those precious books. I could not help being moved as I opened volume after volume which never before had been touched, much less read. In many instances pages by the chapter were still stuck or uncut. As I stood before a huge pile of those unread books and browsed through Drummond's *The Ascent of Man,* the last mental picture of the immaculate Charles came before me. He was seated in his plush chair, surrounded by the world's great wisdom (a wisdom that he was not interested in except for illustrations), and he was completely absorbed by *Denominational Distinctives.*

Then I made the discovery.

A brown, cloth-covered letter file, of medium size, lay on the bottom of one of the book crates. I gave it little notice, except to be struck by the thought that with its well worn appearance it looked out of place amid so many shiny, well kept volumes.

The contents revealed twenty-six letters which Charles had received from a former seminary professor, a man who had taught Ancient Languages. Both of us had taken the course, but I had not noticed at the time that Professor Astute displayed an unusual affection for Charles. I was later to learn that the professor had more sense than any of the students gave him credit for.

The shrewd old man had not written the letters at the beginning of his protégé's ministry but had cleverly timed them to prepare the preacher for the most critical responsibility that he would ever face. The professor had done everything in his power to see to it that great things were in store for the idol of his life. At such a critical point there must be no unexpected mishaps. Professor Astute had written warmly and with a frankness not often observed in the ministry. I am now convinced that any man who will apply himself and take seriously his practical advice will become a success. Feeling so deeply about this matter has led me to the conviction that I owe it to the younger men coming along to publish these documents. Of course, carefully concealing the real identity of both Charles and the professor.

Upon concluding the first reading of these papers, I was confronted by another disturbing question, "How did the letter file get into that crate of books?" I discarded two possibilities. First, knowing Charles as I did, I was positive that he would not have kept such letters among his display books. He would more likely have kept them under lock and key. Second, I was quite sure that they were not there by accident.

Who then could have put them in the crate where they were sure to be found and read by me? The answer was obvious. No one but Priscilla Prince could have done so, and she must have had a reason.

After a lapse of a year I wrote to Mrs. Prince (who was now Mrs. King, wife of a successful broker) requesting an appointment. Her reply was gracious and without delay.

Mrs. King, a tall, handsome woman, still in her early forties, greeted me with unrestrained cordiality. With the exception of a streak of gray, which neatly parted her hair, she had changed little since seminary days.

As soon as courtesy would permit, I got to the point. "Mrs. King, among the prize books in Charles's library, I found a series of twenty-six remarkable letters from Professor Astute, who, you will remember, was on the faculty when Charles and I were students at the seminary. I have come to ask your permission to publish those letters. I am convinced they will help the younger men in the ministry to achieve success."

Priscilla King's merry eyes contrasted sharply with the biting words which formed her reply. "Wesley, you are aware that I put those letters in that crate knowing that they would be read by you. You furthermore know that I wanted them in your hands because of your uncanny ability to get things published. Among all of Charles's friends you are the one to see that the job is done." Then, in a confidential sort of way, she drew nearer me and said: "Pardon me while I get something off my mind. It is true that I am no longer directly associated with the ministry. Yet I have high regard for the work of the church. Because of this, I am disturbed about today's preachers."

Her direct manner made me feel uncomfortable and I began to wish that I had not come for a personal visit. It would have been easier to write to her.

She continued: "You men of the ministry are becoming so adept at evasion and pretense that you find it difficult to distinguish reality from fantasy, truth from error. This is not to say that you are bad men, in the sense that Sinclair Lewis's Reverend Elmer Gantry was a bad man. Your salvation would be easier if that were the case. Your weakness has been in permitting a materialistic and success-hungry world to mold the ministry in its own image. Thus the voice of the prophet has been sacrificed and in its place the voice of a secular-minded people has been reproduced and given religious sanction."

I did not interrupt her. The words, though harsh, had the ring of truth. In my best moments, I, too, had held such views.

She had just about unloaded all that she had to say. "In a society such as ours, there must be a saving remnant. There must be a group of people, small though it may be, who have found something to live for other than getting ahead, achieving success, and winning public acclaim."

I squirmed, shuffled my feet, and said nothing.

Her categorical question was, "Is it too much to expect men of God to be that saving remnant?"

I arose and thanked her for giving me the opportunity of publishing the private letters of Professor Astute written to her late husband.

She laughed and then soothed, to some extent, the open wounds by saying: "I am not putting you and your ministerial friends in the same class with Charles. He was the incomparable master. Of course, in Professor Astute he had a shrewd adviser. I am inclined to believe, however, that he would have made the grade without such help. Charles entered the ministry with a well defined set of secular values, and to his death these values never changed."

Thus my visit with Priscilla King (formerly Mrs. Charles Prince) ended. For those readers who may question the propriety of publishing these private letters, let it be said that it is done with the full permission of Charles's beloved companion of fifteen years.

CHAPTER I

My dear Charles:

You probably know by now that I am to be retired from the seminary faculty next May after twenty-eight years of tenure. I have given the best years of my life to the old school, and though there have been several disappointments along the way I would choose the same course if I had my life to live over again.

I have always had a very real affection for you, and since you were a youngster in college I have predicted for you a great and successful future. You were never aware of it, but many times you have been the center of stormy debates among the faculty members. Professors Needle and Goad, especially, disliked you, and in many ways they have attempted (I am glad to say unsuccessfully) to prevent you from getting to the top. I have looked upon you as "my boy," a Paul and Timothy relation. It was under my pastoral ministry that you were converted and that you surrendered your life to preach the glorious gospel of our Lord and Savior Jesus Christ. When you came to the seminary, it required severe discipline on my part to keep from showing undue affection and partiality toward you.

Now that I am about to retire, I can do something my

soul, for many years, has longed to do. I can speak honestly and without reservation concerning those matters that are pertinent to a man's rise in the ministry. How many times have I gritted my teeth and held my voice as I observed the useless routine required at the seminary! How the students endure it year after year is still a mystery to me. The endless memorization of names, dates, and places and the agony of becoming familiar with dead languages are just a few of the sore spots. What about the impractical material in Homiletics, Public Speaking, and Church Efficiency? If a man took such nonsense seriously he would wind up preaching for life in a little place in the backwoods.

Now I am going to tell you something about my past that I have never shared with any other living person. I do this primarily to show you how in earnest I am about your future and also to give you a better idea of why I am qualified to speak so directly on such matters.

Before accepting the position as Associate Professor in Ancient Languages, I had been the pastor of three churches, all of them different in size and general make-up.

The first church that I held was too large for me. It was located in a county-seat town, and among the membership there were many of the most prominent people in the entire county. Just out of school, I was looked upon somewhat as a prodigy, and this was my undoing. Unlike the gradual rise which I have had in mind for you, I stepped into a commanding position right at the beginning. But my youth and inexperience were entirely against me. I had few friends, most of my associates being extremely jealous of the place I had achieved so soon—by the way, this is one of the inevitable prices demanded of anyone who is a success; so you must be prepared for it—and I think they were secretly glad when the final "bust" came.

It humiliates me to think of it even after these years, but I was forced to resign, and with no place to go. My record had been so poor that another church would have been unwise to consider calling me. The resignation was demanded, not over anything of a serious nature, such as a lapse of morals, and so on, but on the basis that I simply did not produce. After two years there were no more pupils in Sunday school, there had been only twenty-five additions to the church, and the finances had fallen off considerably. My chief mistake in this church was that I thought the preparation and delivery of the sermon was the important thing, and this is one of the reasons why I can never forgive the Homiletics Department. Professor Goad and his associates are aware of this existing condition, yet they send men out by the hundreds imbued with the idea of spending hours with their books in the careful preparation of sermons. What rot!

Anyway, I was forced to resign, with a wife and baby and no place to go. Then I did what so many of the men do, I packed up and came back to the seminary to take graduate work, and for this I shall ever be grateful. It was during this period that I learned at firsthand what Paul meant when he said, "All things work together for good to them that love the Lord."

When I completed my work and received my doctor's degree, I accepted the pastorate of the small church composed of working people with which you are familiar. This is the church where your mother and father are still members. During this ministry I was more cautious; I spent less time on sermons and more on the organizations, and this procedure paid great dividends. I found these people responsive and easy to work with. However, one must think of his family, and their future associations, as well as of his own success. So, after five happy years, I accepted a call which I felt I now deserved, one that I was sure would demand my full talents, and one which I was confident I could handle.

In all my life I was never more mistaken about anything. The call was to a large city church with a complete staff of six assistants. The individuals who "ran" the church were the most domineering and demanding souls I have ever worked with. Their expectations of what one man could do were completely out of reason. Every bit of the work was highly organized, graded, and systematized. The one dominant note was that "last year's record must be surpassed." The quality of the work done, even in this large church, was not even considered. Turning into the Association a better report than the one of the previous year was the thing that mattered. I lived in constant dread because the official Board kept holding over my head the successful administration of previous pastors. (I have since learned that my predecessors, for the most part, were hated as much as I, and that they had just as rough sailing. Oh, how I wish I had known such things when I was in desperate need!)

At the end of six mad years, I was exhausted, defeated, and ready to give up. For the first and only time, I considered the possibility of leaving the ministry. There was one difference between this and my first church: here I had been able to put on a front, and to hide an ugly situation. Not only so, but I discovered that some of the prominent leaders, who were after me, also desired to keep the trouble as quiet as possible. A church can get a reputation for such things, and this can be detrimental to the work of the Kingdom.

However, the showdown was approaching. What could

I do? Could I endure the humiliation of another "forced resignation"? I didn't think I could. When the Board met, I was never more stunned in my life. Instead of asking bluntly for my resignation, as my first church had done, one of the strongest leaders of the opposition arose and made a motion. "I move, Brother Chairman," he said, "that, in the face of Dr. Astute's faithful service over a period of six years, we give him a 'Sabbatical leave' in order that he may travel abroad for a year."

I was so completely overwhelmed by this stroke of strategy that I remained speechless throughout the entire Board meeting. It was obvious that they were giving me an opportunity to save face. In the course of a year, I could find other work and they could find a more suitable pastor.

So I went abroad at the expense of the church. My wife and I traveled in England, France, Italy, Egypt, and the Holy Land. This fruitful trip almost healed the wounds of those crushing six years. Upon returning I was invited to give a series of lectures at the seminary on "The Deplorable Spiritual Condition of the People Abroad." At the conclusion of my week's visit on the campus, the president offered me the position of Associate Professor of Ancient Languages. Again I thanked God that I had gotten my doctor's degree, which qualified me for a place on the faculty. Here I have been for twenty-eight years, and to this day not one of my colleagues has the slightest notion of the hell I endured those six years of my last pastorate.

So you see why I consider myself in a position to advise you. Someone must shepherd these tremendous churches, and I still am of the opinion that it can be done if a man is aware at the time of what to do in specific situations. The purpose of these letters is to do just that. Some of the things I suggest will sound silly, insignificant, and trivial. But they are the very points that the seminary training overlooks, and they are also the ones that you will find most helpful.

Of course you will keep whatever I say to you in the strictest confidence.

Your partner in Christ,

Astute

CHAPTER II

My dear Charles:

As I warned you, many of the suggestions which I shall make will sound exceedingly trivial, but I happen to know that failing to observe these simple things has tripped many an otherwise strong man.

I want to begin with your appearance. Unlike myself, you have splendid material to work with. You will discover many times what a great asset your two-hundred-pound six-foot frame can be. I am not thinking so much about the impression such a build may make on the ladies (they can be won in a variety of ways), I am thinking particularly about the men. A preacher of small build and weak voice is foredoomed, as far as the men are concerned. In all seriousness, such limitations impose an obstacle almost impossible for the average preacher to overcome. The men in the membership prefer thinking of their pastor as being a real he-man, the baseball or football type. Not that you must be rough in appearance: the opposite is true. A man can be big and striking in appearance without looking like a prize fighter.

You have a tendency toward flabbiness and this you must carefully watch. Two simple rules will take care of this:

sensible dieting and moderate exercising. As to the dieting, you should avoid bread, potatoes, and sweets. Stomach muscles can be kept strong by getting fifteen minutes of vigorous setting-up exercises every morning. Under no circumstances should you ever permit your weight to exceed 210. Discipline yourself to these exercises even if it means curtailing your private devotions.

Concerning your clothes I must say "Wear the best." Though you have not gone as far as you will go, you are presently holding a very important church. Most of your people are cultured beyond the average. Store clothes are vastly inferior to tailor-made clothes, and for the few dollars' difference the tailor-made clothes should get the preference every time. At one hundred dollars a suit you can well afford at least ten changes. Since you and Priscilla have no children, you must spend your money some way, and I can think of no wiser investment. Wear only white shirts, properly laundered and starched. Choose your ties with the greatest of taste. I am not referring simply to matching colors but rather to the type: not too loud and not too reserved. There is a happy medium here that you must learn; especially is this true when you go into the pulpit. Your underwear should also be chosen with care. Why? On various occasions you will be stopping at hotels with some of your more prominent men. At such times it will be to your advantage to be well groomed from the skin out.

Your beard is heavy, and of course this presents a nasty problem. Would you be offended if I said that you ought to shave not less than twice every day? The last time I saw you, you were speaking at a Kiwanis Ladies' Night Banquet, and you were not as cleanly shaven as you ought to have been. I could tell that you had attempted to camouflage the evening shadows with talcum powder, but this was not enough. You must watch this.

Avoid too much jewelry. A small diamond ring ought to be the limit. Of course, the fraternity pin I gave you can be worn rather inconspicuously on the vest. But anything beyond this should be taboo.

Select your barber as you do your doctor, and keep your eyes open for dandruff and falling hair. A flabby stomach and a bald or semi-bald head will add fifteen years to your appearance. When you find an excellent barber, who understands your specific needs, stay with him. If you have to wait thirty minutes or an hour to get his chair, wait without getting impatient; it will be time well spent. You will be most fortunate if this particular barbershop has a crew of expert shine boys who take their job seriously; you know how necessary it is to keep the shoes groomed at all times. A manicure once in a while will help. Don't make it a regular practice unless it can be given in privacy behind a curtain. It doesn't look too good for a preacher to be seen getting a manicure once a week.

There is no place in a seminary curriculum for such things to be discussed, but everybody ought to take a bath at least once a day, including preachers. While I am on this subject a word should be said about the care of teeth and under-arm perspiration. I suggest that you keep dental floss, an extra toothbrush, tooth paste, and mouth wash at your study. Most of the time you do not get home for lunch. Thus you go the entire day without attending to your mouth, which, unless great care is exercised, can become a serious drawback. You can never know the full meaning of this until you attempt to deliver a sermon through store teeth. As to the body odors, slight or great, such an offense is inexcusable. It is more inexcusable now than ever before because on every hand there is an ample supply of deodorants.

Though the temptation is great, avoid all perfumes and strong powders.

Yours in His service,

Astute

P.S. "Table manners" is a delicate subject for many people. At the banquet to which I referred, I was gratified to notice that you used a knife and fork with expert finesse. Of course this is highly important at the present, but when you get to the place I have in mind for you one slip with either the knife or the fork would prove fatal.

CHAPTER III

Dear Charles:

A word about your personality. Again, unlike myself you have a great deal of raw material to work with. However, just as there are handicaps in possessing an introvertish nature, there are also serious dangers for the extrovert. To a certain extent I was able to overcome some of the drawbacks involved in my own peculiar personality weakness, and I hope you are going to do an even better job.

Being a natural extrovert, you must be on your guard about several important things. For instance (and I hope you will take this good-naturedly), you are inclined to monopolize a conversation. I am sure you realize how important it is "to get the other person's viewpoint." Yet I have noticed on occasions, even when just the two of us were together, that you were completely absorbed with your own problems and experiences. I believe there is such a ministerial weakness as "audio-mania"; this is the expression I use in describing certain men who talk incessantly. They are in love with, and are hypnotized by, the sound of their own voices. By all means watch this!

Another thing. You take suggestions easily, and this can be good or bad. You can see at once the danger in being easily influenced. Our denomination, along with several others, is presently being torn by two irreconcilable forces, and some of the younger men have already departed from our traditional heritage. I am convinced you have too much respect for the denomination to let this happen in your own case. Just the same, you must constantly be alerted to the possibility of being influenced in the wrong direction.

Along with this is the ever prevalent habit of making snap decisions. Of course, you have been saved the agony which I have had to endure—that of spending endless days and weeks making up my mind about every question I was ever confronted with. On the other hand quick decisions can get you into a lot of hot water. From some of the experiences you have shared with me, I know you have already discovered this at firsthand. Keep this in mind, particularly as you work with your boards and committees. When your opinion is asked for on a controversial subject, learn to say: "There are several sides to this issue. I must have more time to consider every possible angle." This has several advantages. For one thing you will have an opportunity to view the situation objectively; but even more important than that, you will discover that the people who put you on the spot with a delicate problem will forget all about it within a week. In such cases there is no point in pursuing the matter.

"We want a pastor with personality. If he does not have personality, whatever else he has does not matter." This is the opinion held by many church leaders today, especially in the stronger churches. You can judge for yourself how serious the matter is. In analyzing what such people mean by "personality" we discover that it can be reduced to the simplest possible terms.

Let me illustrate by asking you a question, "Whom do you enjoy being with more than anyone else?" Answer: The people who help you feel good, who build you up, and make you feel important. They do this by picking out one or more specific characteristics to call attention to, sometimes using a well chosen compliment. It really is as simple as that.

One final word of caution. Do not let your gregarious nature trap you. The normal desire for most people is to have several close and intimate friends. This is just one of the many sacrifices that a minister must make. You cannot afford to become intimately friendly with anyone in your church or community. To do so is fatal. Once the news gets around that the Princes and the Drews, or the Princes and the Joneses are as "thick as they can be," you have approached the beginning of the end. After trying it both ways, I have concluded that such pleasures are simply not worth the price involved. I question the wisdom of you and Priscilla ever accepting a dinner engagement from any of your parishioners. If you do accept, then by all means do not return the invitation. Several experiences such as this will completely solve the problem.

Yours in Christ,

Astute

CHAPTER IV

Dear Charles:

I must elaborate a little more on how to take advantage of every bit of the personality you possess. As you know, the sweetest word in the English language is the sound of your own name. If that be true, then there is only one thing to do: *Memorize the name of every person on your church roll,* including their first names.

I can see the astonishment in your face as you read this. You think it is an impossible task. Your church has an enrollment of seventeen hundred members, men, women, and children. Of that seventeen hundred, six hundred cannot be found; they are dead timber. Of the eleven hundred left, three hundred contribute but never attend (this includes several dozen non-resident members). That reduces the number to eight hundred, and of these not more than 50 per cent attend more than once a month. Now it is the remaining four hundred that I am referring to when I insist on your memorizing every name. This is not an insurmountable task.

Recall, if you will, the Greek and Hebrew conjugations and declensions that you memorized by the ream. What about those outlines in theology and the points in the harmony of the gospels, not to mention committing to memory every overnight stop in Paul's four or five journeys across the Roman Empire? Compared with this, memorizing four hundred names is a simple assignment.

It is an incomparable advantage to be able to call people by name as you shake hands with them at the conclusion of the various services, or as you meet them on the street. It is not a bad thing for your people to be able to say proudly to members of a rival congregation, "Our pastor can call by name *every* member of the church. The other night, for instance, at a banquet of more than seventy-five people, he asked permission to test himself, and believe me he did not miss a single name!" That reputation, my boy, is worth more than any grade you ever made in Greek or Hebrew!

It is also a good thing to write personal notes to those who have received some recognition in the community, or who have had some unusual experience. At least one morning of the week should be entirely devoted to this. Birthdays, wedding anniversaries, graduations, promotions, making the team, and so on, should not go unnoticed. A few words in your own hand will be worth many times more than a typewritten sheet.

There ought not to be any slips in this practice. But mistakes can happen. One of the most stupid things I ever did was in this connection. For years I made it a practice to write such notes, particularly to the men who had been in my classes. It was the best tie that I had with those who had gone out from our institution. On one occasion, while I was returning from a convention, I noticed on the back cover of a book which I had been reading the advertisement of a new volume by one of my former pupils. Right there on the train one of those snap decisions struck me. I took out my pen and wrote a brief complimentary note to the author. Of course, I used general terms, but it was enough to humiliate me none the less. I simply said that I was very proud of my former pupil, that the book was well written and to the point, and that in every way it lived up to my expectations of him. What I failed to notice, in extremely small type at the bottom of the advertisement, were the words, "To be published in March" (two months later).

Fifteen years have passed since then, and I have not completely lived down the blunder. There is no excuse for permitting a thing like that to happen.

In His service,

Astute

CHAPTER V

Dear Charles:

Concerning certain personal habits I have this to say. These will be determined more by the community in which you live and the kind of church you serve than by anything else.

As a general rule, however, the use of tobacco in any form should be eliminated. It disturbs me that many of the men, on our side, and men who are sound in the faith and loyal to the denomination, have taken to this iniquitous habit. Believe it or not, last year we had in the student body two men who chewed tobacco. Of course, they were straight from the hills and did not know any better, but imagine a preacher of the gospel with a wad of chewing tobacco in his mouth!

My primary reason for suggesting that you forego the use of tobacco is a very practical one. During the course of a six- or eight-year pastorate, many of your natural weaknesses will come to light. These will furnish your opposition sufficient things to shoot at. I have never seen the sense in giving them additional targets, particularly when so little is at stake. If you ask me what stand you should take on this as far as the church members are concerned, I would have to answer that it all depends on circumstances. Once I had, in the same church, a chairman of the Board, a treasurer, and a Sunday-school superintendent who did not use tobacco in any form whatsoever. Thus in several sermons I bore down sharply on this question. On the other hand, in my last church, every leading official of the church, including their wives, sons, and daughters, smoked. Under such circumstances I would have been a fool to make an issue out of so small a matter.

Profanity and slang of course are not a part of a good minister's vocabulary. There are acceptable ways of using "damn" and "hell" in the pulpit, but this will have to do. There are certain members who like to hear the pastor use these words occasionally. It gives them the feeling that he is "human." But by and large they should be deleted from all conversation. As to slang, this too can be hurtful. If you must say something to let the people know that you are not stiff and formal, use "Doggone." In most quarters this is light, acceptable, and will serve the purpose.

Jokes should be handled with great care. Of course, you will never tell a joke of any kind from the pulpit. There you are preaching the gospel and wrestling with lost souls. It is no time to be humorous. On the other hand when you appear before conventions and clubs you must create some levity. Jokes on yourself are always good; anything suggestive (you know what I mean) must never be used. If you are in certain sections of the country, Negro stories always get a laugh. "There was a Negro preacher who had a big congregation, and so on." You want to be careful of this. It may fall flat on its face before some groups, especially college students.

Do not be inveigled into playing cards of any kind or description. I can think of nothing that spells "sudden death" in larger letters than getting the reputation of being a "bridge-playing preacher." In a way it is fortunate that you and Priscilla do not have any children. Many times they create unsolvable problems for the conscientious pastor. With us, our daughter insisted on playing cards. She even sneaked them into the parsonage. Imagine my embarrassment on one occasion when the president of the Ladies' Aid pulled a deck of cards from under a sofa pillow! It is silly to jeopardize your position over so small a matter. Remember, no cards of any kind (with the possible exception of Rook, and this will vary according to the community you live in).

In the same manner, you should determine the feeling of the community toward playing golf. In recent years it has become more acceptable for preachers to play golf along with the other professional men in the community. I can remember the time, however, when to do so was considered a lack of spirituality. In certain communities it is still so considered. A "golf-playing" preacher may be as bad as a "bridge-playing" preacher.

In Jesus' name,

Astute

CHAPTER VI

Dear Charles:

Concerning the Sabbath, you should hold the people strictly to the fourth commandment. We are getting away from this, and the churches, as well as the denomination, are suffering because of it. The way some Christians desecrate Sunday afternoon is almost more than I can take! Excuse me for referring to the last church I served, but so many things happened there that keep coming before me. I had people in that church, deacons and circle chairmen, who thought nothing of going on a Sunday afternoon picnic or going to the club to swim or even playing golf. To combat this I tried to arrange a meeting of some kind every Sunday afternoon at the church. I must confess it did not work too well, but it was a step in the right direction. Perhaps you can do better.

With delinquency rising every year, dancing among the young people must be condemned more forcefully than ever. You can be thankful that you still have the opinion of the denomination on your side in this matter. As you know, at our great regional summer assembly I got through the resolution prohibiting, not only dancing among the young people, but also mixed bathing. It is the practice now for the girls to swim from ten to twelve in the morning and the boys from two to four in the afternoon. This simple plan has solved one of the most serious problems connected with our great assembly.

Frequently you will find a youngster who will want to argue with you about dancing. He may say that there can't be much harm in it because he enjoys dancing with his sister or even his mother. Listen to him patiently but hold your ground firmly. You and I know what an eighteen-year old boy is thinking about when he has in his arms a semi-clothed voluptuous creature of his own age. These thoughts and images are accentuated when the two warm bodies are brought closely together in a rhythmic embrace.

While we are on this delicate subject, I should like to make a suggestion concerning your staff and the arrangement of your study. You will have one or more secretaries. By all means these should not be under fifty, and the more efficient and the less attractive in appearance they are, the better it will be for you. Church people have acquired a well earned reputation for gossip. Such gossip can be extremely detrimental. In case you do not know it, some church leaders, when they get desperate in their attempt to "move a pastor," will resort to circulating unfounded rumors. No charges, just rumors, will get the job done quickly and efficiently.

Along with this advice is the matter of the arrangement of your study. You may have the most expensive decorations and furnishings that money can buy, but by all means do not include in the furnishings anything resembling a sofa or couch. Remember this. Whenever a woman has an appointment with you, regardless of the nature of the matter to be discussed, see to it that one of your secretaries is in a position to see and hear everything that is said. If necessary, the door to your study can always be left ajar. You may not have many people seeking your help if you follow this plan, but you must not take unnecessary risks. If you find this impractical, I suggest that you get a tape recorder, conceal it in your desk, and take down every word of every interview.

Many of these points will sound a little narrow and overzealous. But you do not have to be afraid of that; you have a powerful weapon that gives you deserved recognition regardless of your views. What is that weapon? you ask. By now you have discovered on many occasions what a blessed thing it was to take your graduate work. At the time I had to high-pressure you into doing it; you thought you knew enough without it. And from the angle of "knowing enough" you were right. But I was aware of something that you did not know. A Ph.D. will open more doors and make more of an impression than anything you could possibly possess. This is especially true where there are people in the congregation who have been to college or who are associated with one of the educational systems. As businessmen have gold dust in their veins, school people are degree-conscious to a pitiable state; their very existence depends on being so. Many jokes are made of rank-worshiping military personnel, but the military is outdone by school people. This you will learn. Now, with a Ph.D. you can command the respect of people, regardless of certain unpopular views which you may hold.

By the way, I want to suggest that you destroy your present stationery and get a fresh supply printed and omit the Ph.D. after your name. When you first started out it was necessary to get established as Dr. Prince, rather than Reverend or Mr. (or that abominable "Brother"). Now that this has been accomplished, it would be far better to have your name appear simply as *Charles P. Prince* without any "handle" whatsoever.

This will create a very favorable effect as far as many of your associates are concerned. Here is a man, pastor of an outstanding church and a Ph.D., who does not even bother to put the degree after his name! Modesty and humility, Charles, are two indispensable traits of a good minister of Jesus Christ. As I have told my classes many, many times, if a pastor does not possess these virtues he might as well get out of the ministry.

In the spirit of Christ,

Astute

CHAPTER VII

Dear Charles:

In my last letter I failed to mention an important item about your visitation program. I am well aware that "pastoral visiting" is almost a thing of the past as far as city pastors are concerned. However, I have insisted, in spite of my tragic experiences, that the job can be done, particularly if a man knows what to do and if he will apply himself conscientiously. Visiting the membership as a means toward receiving the full confidence of the people is absolutely indispensable. There is no substitute for it. If you had three or four assistant pastors, that still would not solve the problem. They want *you* to come to see them.

I know all the excuses and alibis; but none are worth the time it takes to recite them. "People are not at home these days"; "The blaring radio prevents an intelligent visit"; "Only the women and children are contacted in this way"; "There are so many other things to do"; ad infinitum.

The plain fact is that the majority of pastors simply do not like this part of their work, and I am beginning to suspect that that includes you. However, with your free and easy manner this should not be at all difficult. What if you had an inferiority complex such as plagued me in my early ministry? When I accepted my first church (the one that was too big for me) I was scared to death of people. Calling on a family was worse, many times worse than conducting a funeral. I sweat blood over visiting, and that is why I know what I am talking about. Had I not fallen for the "assistant pastor" idea in my last pastorate, my years of greater usefulness in the church would have been increased. Perhaps I would not have spent twenty-eight years of my life teaching dead languages to thousands of disinterested students.

You have the drive; all that is necessary is for you to see the importance of this responsibility. To simplify the task, I suggest that you have your secretary type a separate roll book for your personal use. Classify the membership alphabetically and according to the streets where they live. Be sure that these streets are also listed alphabetically and the house numbers arranged numerically. With this book in your car you should spend two hours a day, five days out of every week, visiting your flock. Now let us see where that brings us. Ten minutes per visit is long enough. In the olden days such a brief visit would have been an insult, but now things have changed. Allowing for a few minutes to get from one house to another—instead of hopping from one section of town to another, on Monday you visit all the homes on Roosevelt Boulevard; on Tuesday you take those on Truman Street, and so on—you should get in at least five visits per hour, which makes ten visits a day. This means fifty visits a week. In an eleven-month year (August you are on vacation recuperating) you will have got in 2,550 visits, in five years 12,650, simply by devoting two hours a day, five days a week. With what results? You will fill your auditorium in the morning and double your attendance at night. But what is infinitely more important than this, you will have endeared yourself to your membership to an unbelievable degree. *They will literally worship you.* During my first pastorate I followed one of those "visiting preachers"; so I know at firsthand how the people remember such efforts. Whether or not you can deliver a sermon will increasingly mean less to them.

No, Charles, in spite of the misleading contentions of Professors Needle and Goad, the preparation and delivery of sermons is the simplest part of your work. Unless you become controversial, which I trust your good judgment will prevent, your congregations will rarely hear anything you say. In fact, they have heard it so often that they know what you are going to say before you say it. If they should happen to catch a few words here and there, it would make very little difference as far as their living is concerned. For the most part, they have pretty well made up their minds what kind of people they prefer to be.

The point is, you have visited them, your congregations have more than doubled, and the people love you. And after all, that is the only thing that matters. Without their love and confidence, your hands are tied; you can accomplish very little. "Now abideth faith, hope, love, these three, but the greatest of these is love."

Christianly yours,

Astute

P.S. If no one is at home (or if they fail to answer the door) you should do two things: record the date of the visit in your address book, and when you return to your study drop the family a personal note explaining that you called. By all means do not leave a "calling card." This is too cold and impersonal.

CHAPTER VIII

Dear Charles:

From what I have said you might have got the impression that I have little regard for reading and studying. This would be erroneous. I sense the importance of reading, but what I am after is that you read with great selectivity.

Time and again Professors Needle and Goad have revealed how very little they are acquainted with the responsibilities of the pastor. As you know, neither of these men ever held a church. They came to us from other teaching posts. There should be a rule in every seminary to the effect that no man is qualified to teach preachers who himself has not been a preacher. Needle and Goad stress the great importance of study and careful preparation of sermons. But how many endless hours are wasted by men who are trying to be conscientious? After wading through heavy, involved books, what do they have? What more do they know? Are they better able to stir the people? In most instances the answer to these questions is an obvious "No."

Take Toynbee's *A Study of History* as an example. In college you had a minor in history and you took at least three excellent courses in history here at the seminary under Professor Saddle. Of course, you did not learn all there is to know, but who has? By sticking with it for weeks without end, you can at last finish *A Study of History* and then, with the exception of being able to say that you have read it, where has it gotten you? Are you really any better prepared to preach the gospel?

There is a type of reading that is indispensable. Our denomination has its own publishing house, and every month there are available to the pastor who is interested at least forty different periodicals covering every vital subject. If you are not subscribing to these, I urge you to do so without delay. On your desk should be the latest copies of *Home Missions Banner, Foreign Missions Trumpet, State Missions Digest,* the *Sunday School Restorer,* the *Cradle Roll Builder,* the *Studenteer* (for college students), *Life in the Home* (dealing with family problems), the *Brotherhood Journal, Woman's Work, Training Program* (for the Sunday evening work). There are several others, but these are the essential ones. (There is a nondenominational weekly called the *Christian Unlimited* which is a waste of both time and money.) You can keep up with "pastoral changes" and what is going on in our region by subscribing to three of our own state papers: the *Biblical Bugle,* the *Biblical Trumpet,* and the *Biblical Clarinet.*

In addition to these periodicals there are "study course" books covering every phase of our church life. There are approximately sixty of these books in all the courses, and you should have more than a speaking acquaintance with each one; you should master all of them. Teach them to your people, and see that a careful record is made of every single award secured during your pastorate.

Sermon books constitute another type of reading material which can prove beneficial, if handled correctly. I said "handled correctly." Choose your men wisely, and know what you are looking for. In another letter I will deal with this at more length.

I come now to make a serious request of you. Do not read Fosdale. We discourage the use of his books in our classes here at the seminary, and there is a rule prohibiting the displaying of any of his books in our denominational bookstores. Thus it is likely that up to the present you have never been exposed to the writings of this man. However, sooner or later you will meet a preacher on the other side who exclaims, "Have you read Fosdale's this, that, and the other?" Charles, there is no man among us who has disturbed the faith of so many, and there is certainly no man living or dead who has hurt our denomination as Fosdale has. He is one of the most persuasive men that Satan has ever used. He slips up on you from behind, and before you realize it you are agreeing with some impossible position. Since he is so persuasive, I am making you this simple, but serious, request.

Many years ago, when you were a little fellow, I preached a sermon on the "Blessings of Prohibition." Following that sermon, I distributed cards to those present challenging each and every one to sign his name, pledging never to touch a drop of alcoholic beverages in any form. You were among those present, and it did my heart good to know that you were among the first to sign up. Now I am making a similar request. In your next letter, I want you to promise me, in writing, that you will never read anything that Fosdale has ever written. This will relieve my mind no little. I regret that before now I have not possessed the courage to discuss this matter with you.

May the Holy Spirit guide you,

Astute

CHAPTER IX

Dear Charles:

All of us have unrealized ambitions; we cannot be experts in everything. The sooner a man discovers this, the better off he will be. The unhappy people are those who have a strong urge or ambition in a certain direction, but who simply do not have the native capacity to follow through. And believe me, "capacity" is not to be considered lightly. We can improve, but only within the framework of what has been given to us.

I have known for a long time that you have had an urge to write. I strongly advise against it for two reasons: First, when you write you leave a permanent record of what you have thought and said. Such material, sometimes written in the heat of an adolescent mood, can subsequently prove disastrous. Second, you do not have the knack for writing. Forgive me, Charles, for being so blunt. If I hurt you, it is only because I love you.

Several years ago, I picked up one of our Sunday-school quarterlies and noticed that you were the lesson writer for the entire year. I held my breath, expecting the worst, and my misgivings were immediately confirmed. My boy, they were bad; very, very bad. I am sure that several of my first-year students could have done much better. If it will relieve you, in any way, few extroverts ever become effective writers. So you have a lot of company. Men in that group must "be doing something": meeting people, making new plans, engineering great projects. Most pastors of our large churches fall into this classification. Have you ever noticed the scarcity of writing material from our ranks? Aside from a few sermon books (most of them sound in the faith but pitifully weak), we do not produce much material. The two traits simply are not to be found in one personality, and the preference of our church people is strongly in favor of the buoyant extrovert.

Another point that may help relieve the sting of this frustration is the knowledge that writing is the most painful and exhaustive discipline that any man has ever endured. I have tried my hand at it a few times, and I know whereof I speak. Imagine endless hours behind a typewriter that often grins and laughs at you because the needed words will not come forth—not to mention the pain of correcting, editing, and rewriting. Added to this is the terrible suspense of not knowing how people will interpret what you have written. Yes, you can easily get writing out of your system if you remember these few details.

Of course, there is nothing wrong in letting your people know "that Dr. Prince is writing a book." It need never be published, but the mere fact that you are "working on a book" lends a scholarly atmosphere that can be of help in some situations.

This is a common practice around the seminary. Professors Side and Saddle for years "have been coming out with a new book." Up to the present the books have not been produced, but as far as I can tell no harm has been done.

Upon my retirement in May, I hope to be able to visit

with you for a few days. There are several things that I am anxious to discuss with you in person. You have been at your present church for five years, and your record is unsurpassed by any of our men. I have a premonition that the most strategic church in all our territory will be open some time in the near future. You deserve the full consideration of the pulpit committee, and I am going to see that you get it.

These things we will discuss when I have the privilege of visiting you. In my great anticipation, there is one insignificant shadow about which very little can be done. For several years I have felt that Priscilla dislikes me intensely. I have not held this against her nor have I permitted her coldness to mar the friendship that has endured between you and me through the years. (See Romans 12:20.)

May the love of Christ be with you,

Astute

CHAPTER X

Dear Charles:

In recent letters I have made some suggestions about your reading and writing; now I want to share with you what information I have concerning the preparation and delivery of sermons. As you know, this is Professor Goad's department, but, like so many professors of public speaking and homiletics, he has never been a pastor. So I do not think it immodest of me to assume that I know a few things that he does not know.

As I inferred a little while ago, the lives of very few people are changed through preaching. They simply do not hear what you are saying, or if they hear they usually know "what comes next." This is not such a disadvantage as it may sound. So long as there are no "kick-backs," no explosions of any kind, what have you to complain about? There is a type of preaching that keeps the people on the edges of their seats, but this is no good. Why bring up anything controversial? And what have you gained if you simply succeed in making the people mad at you, or suspicious of you? Absolutely nothing.

There are three types of sermons the people need in this desperate hour. First, sermons of comfort. The world is in a mess. There are more people drinking and carousing now than ever before. Many of your members have burdens too heavy for them to bear. They are tired, worn, and exhausted. They have been overcome by a fatigue which has drained them of life and strength. This includes your well-to-do members just as much as your poor ones. Really, I sometimes do not know in which group there is a larger number of "tired ones," the rich or the poor. But I do know, they all need fortification. Throughout the Bible there are sufficient texts on this theme to keep you preaching the rest of your ministry.

Second, there is a great need for Bible or "expository" preaching. This can be difficult, but it can also be effective. There is nothing more helpful than gaining the reputation of being a "Bible preacher." You must someday try preaching through the entire Bible verse for verse beginning with the first chapter of Genesis. There is one word of caution about Bible preaching. Let the people make the applications for themselves. For example, assume that they have enough sense to know why Jesus deliberately chose a Samaritan as the hero of one of his famous stories. I see no point whatsoever in making the application from the pulpit that the Jew-Samaritan relation in Jesus' day was almost identical with the white-Negro relation today. Simply assume that the people have sense enough to make such applications for themselves.

The third type of sermon is that of a strongly evangelistic nature. Here you must be at your best, and I suggest that if your Sunday-evening congregation is as small as in some places, you ought to begin preaching more evangelistic sermons in the morning. Not many lost souls attend church on Sunday evening any more, and it looks now as if fewer will be attending the morning service in the future. Of course, you can always depend on your Sunday school to supply this need. Contrary to what Professor Needle emphasizes, the Sunday school is not a school in any sense of the word. It is an agency, a medium through which you get 90 per cent of your additions. Lost people, in Sunday school, will more likely attend the morning service than the evening service. You can easily see the dire implications in not taking advantage of this evangelistic opportunity.

How will this suit the congregation? you ask. Aside from those who need fortification *every* Sunday, it will overwhelmingly meet with their approval. It helps to destroy a suspicion that creeps in many minds ever so often. Above everything else, most of us want to be convinced that "I am saved." Can you think of a better way of drilling this into the subconscious minds of your people than by directing all your big guns toward "the lost?" This does not mean to say that your people are totally unaware of how grievously they sin during the week; it simply means that you have helped them not to consider the matter too seriously. Their attention and energy are now directed toward the "unsaved." And believe me, this is one time they will sit back and pray for you to pour it on those who are outside the fold. There is absolutely no substitute for evangelistic fervor. Once again, with a Ph.D. you can afford to do what many, in the college situations, now discourage.

Concerning preparation, I suggest the works of Spurgeon, Moody, Torrey, and Edwards. As you absorb this material do not make the mistake of using the same subject and text of these great sermons. Some of the men do this, and I think the practice is unforgivable. It came to my attention some time ago that one of my students, now in the field, has grown so listless that he does not even take the time to make his own notes. His deacons discovered him sneaking Moody's sermons into the pulpit with him, verbatim. He did this by taking a razor blade, cutting the sermons out, and inserting them between the pages of his pulpit Bible.

No, what you must do is to change the subjects and texts and make your own outlines. It is to your advantage not to take notes of any kind into the pulpit with you. The books that I have referred to are lucid with illustrations, and these constitute your greatest preaching asset. Every sermon should contain not less than three well chosen illustrations: one to begin with, one just before the people's attention has wandered completely, and one to close with. The last, of course, is infinitely more important than the other two. This is the one the people who have listened will take home with them.

Yours in Christ's Service,

Astute

P.S. It is possible that you may have received the impression that I do not highly regard my own department of Ancient Languages. Of course, in many ways I have despised this work all these twenty-eight years, but there are compensations for everything. As you know, one of the undergirding doctrines of our faith is "Once saved, always saved." There is positively no such thing as falling from grace or falling away. There are too many scriptures which substantiate this doctrine. However, in the New Testament, Hebrews 6:4–6, the Scriptures clearly read for all to see, "For it is impossible for those who were once enlightened, and have tasted of the heavenly gift, and were made partakers of the Holy Ghost, and have tasted the good word of God, and the powers of the world to come; if they should fall away, to renew them again unto repentance, seeing they crucify to themselves the Son of God afresh, and put him to an open shame." I have often thought that the divine writer could have just as easily omitted these words. But since he did not, you men who have gone through my classes can always say to a doubting member, "These words mean something entirely different in the Greek, and unless you have at least a fragmentary knowledge of the original they are difficult to explain."

CHAPTER XI

Dear Charles:

Under no circumstances, and for no reason, perform the ceremony of a divorced person. In our denomination there is no binding rule upon the clergy in such matters. Every man must set his own policy. If the New Testament were clearer on this subject perhaps there would not be so much misunderstanding. But, whether the people are aware of it, you and I know that it is not clear. Though I would not say it from the pulpit, Paul is not to be trusted implicitly when he talks about marriage. Being single, he wished all people were as he; however, if they could not stand this condition, or could not contain themselves (I believe Paul uses the vulgar expression "keep from burning"), then, and then only, should marriage take place. This seems to put this holy relation on a pretty low level.

And when Jesus says, "If a man would put away his wife let him give her a bill of divorcement," we are once again confused. Every New Testament student knows that Jesus was hitting at the prevalent Jewish practice of the male putting away his wife without taking the trouble to give her a bill of divorcement. Being "put away" without a bill of divorcement meant that the woman was disgraced and also meant that she was ineligible for remarriage. If, under those circumstances, she did remarry, both she and the man she was living with were considered living in adultery. However, in this scripture it is obvious that Jesus was pleading with the arrogant males to deal more kindly with their wives. These women, with whom they had grown tired, should not be "put away," but should be given a bill of divorcement. The only wife not entitled to that important bill of divorcement was a woman who had degraded her marriage vow by being unfaithful to her husband. However, all others who were "put away" and given a "bill of divorcement" (a clean slate) were eligible for remarriage.

Having known for some time that this is a more accurate interpretation of those verses from the Sermon on the Mount, I still refuse to marry divorced people. Neither have I been influenced by learning that Professor Saddle's father, who was one of the most distinguished professors this institution has ever had, was a divorced man (Professor Saddle being the old man's son by his second wife).

My refusal to marry divorced people is a very personal one. I shudder to think of performing the ceremony of divorced persons who might come to me with such a request. Imagine the lives that many of them have lived! However, once you begin the practice there is no stopping. Not even Solomon would know where to draw the line.

One of the few disagreements that I have ever had with Professor Saddle is on this very subject. He will marry divorced couples, but only those with "scriptural grounds." By "scriptural grounds" I presume he means that the divorce was granted on the grounds of adultery and that he is marrying the innocent party. Of course he is marrying the innocent party! How many people do you know who ever confessed to being the *guilty* one in such cases? A woman will admit every other sin, but she will deny as long as possible that she ever had intercourse with any man other than her husband. In such cases Professor Saddle becomes not only preacher but jury and judge. He hears the evidence (usually only one side) and then solemnly decides to perform or not perform the ceremony.

The only safe policy is to refuse to marry any divorced person. This will save a lot of embarrassment. As sure as you break over and marry one couple, the very next person who requests your services will be the divorced daughter of the chairman of the Board of Deacons, and though she may not have "scriptural grounds" *you marry her or else!* However, if your policy is the refusal to marry divorced people, under any circumstances, this is usually taken quite well. In many cases profound admiration results. "Dr. Prince is a man of real conviction" is the word that gets around. Thus, instead of being hindered, you are really boosted.

I must confess that there have been times when the shallowness of this policy has disturbed me no little. I once refused to marry a young man, a remarkable fellow who has since made good in many ways, including that of his second marriage. He is still a faithful member of the church where I was pastor at the time of his divorce. (Had he been a Catholic, the church would have done the consistent thing and excluded him; however, we refuse to marry such people but retain them in the church in good standing though their second marriage might have been performed by a justice of the peace.) The very next week following my refusal to marry this divorced party, I performed two weddings. One was a girl five months pregnant by a man other than the one she was marrying. The other a boy who, I later learned, was eaten up with a venereal disease. (This was long before blood tests were required.) In neither of these incidents did I break my rule of marrying a "divorced party." In the first case the girl had not bothered to marry the soldier boy (World War I); she just lived with him until she got pregnant, and upon his leaving the States she went back to the man who loved her. I performed this ceremony so that the poor little baby could have a name. In the second case I knew the boy was a rounder, but I also knew he had never been married and therefore never divorced. So, as far as my books were concerned, I was conscience-free to perform his ceremony.

Though this policy is shallow in places, I still prefer it to that of Professor Saddle's impossible rule, "I will for some, but not for others."

This is a knotty problem, and it is possible that I may have confused you more than helped you. However, whether or not you understand all the implications, determine once for all that you will never perform the ceremony of any divorced person. Regardless of what happens, I think you will find this the *safest* position, and after all this is what matters.

Scripturally yours,

Astute

CHAPTER XII

Dear Charles:

Tithing will solve all your problems. Does that sound strange? Let it sound stranger still when I say that there is no problem on earth, in heaven, or hell that tithing will not solve. The principle behind this is a very simple one. The majority of the men who run our churches are successful businessmen. These men have come to respect one thing above all else: a successful business administration, whether it is in a store, government, or church. The old saying, "There is nothing that succeeds like success," is doubly fitting when applied to a church.

There are two possible approaches, and you must be careful about using the first one. However, I found it acceptable, and profitable, in my second church (the one where I knew five happy years). The never ending theme is from the Old Testament, "Bring ye all the tithes into the storehouse, and see if the Lord will not pour you out blessings from heaven that you cannot contain." The appeal in this is that if you trust the Lord and put in ten dollars you will get twenty in return. This may sound a little materialistic, but it gets results. For obvious reasons this approach would not have worked in either of my other two pastorates. However, with the second it did work, and it is just as effective today. Churches have tremendous financial obligations, local, state, national, and foreign; these obligations demand large sums of money; this money can be raised easily and efficiently if everyone will tithe. You may not get everyone to tithe, but you will get sizable increases in subscriptions, and this is primarily what you are concerned with.

Let me illustrate what tithing will do. In your membership of seventeen hundred there are at least eight hundred separate incomes. These incomes annually will average not less than $3,800, including the women who work. Of course, there are many who make much more than this, but there are just as many who earn $1,800 and $2,000. The average ought to be near $3,800. If every one of these eight hundred wage earners tithed, that would give your church an annual budget of $197,600! Your present budget of $80,000 is excellent, but look what it might be! There is no goal or objective your church could not reach; there is no problem that would not be solved if this plan became efficiently operative. It gives me a feeling of elation just to think of the unlimited possibilities. Tithing really works!

Then you must consider the spiritual benefits of this program. I happen to know that in your membership there are two men whose net income last year was not less than $40,000 each. This means that each one of these men should be giving to the church $4,000 per year, or $76.92 per week! Now, when you can get a man who is making $40,000 a year to give $4,000 of that to the church, you have really accomplished something! Why? For the simple reason that "the love of money is the root of all evil." In giving that $4,000 per annum, those evil roots are destroyed, and you have a Christian, one who has "grown in the grace, and knowledge of our Lord and Savior Jesus Christ." It may work a greater hardship on those two men to live on the remaining $36,000 than it will for some of your men to support their families on $3,000.

The Lord bless you real good,

Astute

P.S. It would be detrimental to the cause if your people should discover that according to the Old Testament interpretation of the tithe, nearly all of them could check their cards as tithers. As you know, the tithe to the Jew meant bringing a tenth of the increase that the Lord had given him into the storehouse for distribution according to the needs and responsibilities of the *total* community. This distribution did not stop with the upkeep of the Temple or the support of the priests; it often included everything that we call "civil" or "secular," even the military. Thus our present national government is seeing to it that we all tithe, voluntarily or involuntarily.

There is no use in bringing this up with the people, because it can be confusing.

CHAPTER XIII

Dear Charles:

One of the reasons I have always been attracted to you is that of your natural alertness. Yes, there are some problems that tithing will not solve. If you will reread my last letter you will notice that I said, "Tithing will solve all your problems." What I should have said is, "Tithing will solve any problem *for which there is a solution.*"

The situation which you call to my attention is not serious; it is of your own making and as far as I know there is absolutely no solution to it. You mention the fact that the Skully family will be moving their membership to one of the smaller churches where more working people attend.

I was particularly struck with your description of the many ways by which you attempted to "make these poor people feel at home." You say they were fairly well received by your members. They sang in the choir; Mrs. Skully was in a circle and Sunday-school class; Mr. Skully assisted with one of the young people's organizations. However, in spite of this reception you insist they were not happy in your church, for the reason that this hospitality did not extend beyond the front doors of the church itself. In other words, outside the church building *they were sociably unaccept-*

able as far as your leading members were concerned. The Skullys felt and resented this, and so they decided to leave your church.

Now here is a situation that we must face realistically. People have been that way a long time, and there is nothing in this world that is going to change them. In my repertoire there is absolutely no solution for this problem. The best thing to do is to forget it.

However, there is one little matter that I should like to bring to your attention. You said the Skullys had been members of your church just about two years. Therefore they joined under your ministry. I know that nowadays most people join the church only after they have been contacted by a personal visit with considerable pressure being applied. Usually this visit is made by the pastor, and it is he who wins them to the church. The obvious conclusion is that it was you who created a situation for which there is no solution. I trust it will be a lesson to you. You cannot build a great church out of trash.

In the name of the Nazarene,

Astute

P.S. You have gained a reputation for being "spiritual." Once you have been successful in getting your people to think of you as being "spiritual," there is nothing to fear from then on. I hope this will be just as easily accomplished in your next pastorate. Ordinary people, conscious of their sins and limitations, find it difficult to question or criticize one who they are convinced is "spiritual." To them it is almost like questioning or criticizing the Lord Himself. I have only pity for the preachers who sacrifice this power over their people for a game of bridge or a cigarette.

CHAPTER XIV

Dear Charles:

When your members begin to grow weary with your sermons, or when you have failed to give sufficient personal attention to the people who matter, or when your offerings decrease, your Sunday-school lags, your choir fights, or your congregations dwindle, REMEMBER ONE THING: DIVERT ATTENTION.

When Mussolini got involved in a dozen or more serious domestic problems what did he do? He started a war on tiny Ethiopia. Of course, I am not suggesting that you start a war—there's enough fighting without that. But I am insisting that you know how to divert attention—adroitly, smoothly, with extreme stratagem.

The best way that I can think of accomplishing this is simply by having a successful revival. By successful revival I mean one where there will be reported two hundred additions or more within a period of two weeks. I have seen preachers who apparently were on their last pins, as far as their pastorates were concerned, who managed this thing at the right time in the right way with the result that they were able to hang on five or ten years longer. If, for some inexplicable reason, such a revival does not solve your internal problems, you still have not lost anything. Rather, you will be able to report to the Convention the largest number of additions in your association, state, or perhaps in the entire region. With what result? You will immediately be sought after by dozens of churches that have been reporting fewer and fewer additions.

There are several requirements that must be met if desired objectives are to be achieved. Select your visiting evangelist with great care. *Do not invite a man who can really preach.* If you do, this will jeopardize your position more than ever. Some of the people will be in favor of ousting you immediately and calling the evangelist as their pastor. This, my boy, has happened more than once. Of that I can bear witness.

By the same token you do not want a complete "dud." You want an evangelist who can tell a number of vivid stories, preferably out of his own personal experiences, and one who can give an invitation. In addition to this, he ought to be able to do personal work. There is nothing so effective as selling people in their homes or shops.

By way of preparation, it is a good thing to have as long a prospect list as possible. If your goal is two hundred additions, the list should not be less than five hundred, including the unsaved children. After you get the list prepared—names and addresses—the next thing to do is to arrange cottage prayer meetings all over the city. This will start the people talking about the forthcoming meeting, and it will also give you an opportunity to ask certain of your members to lead these prayer meetings. You, of course, will have sense enough to know which members to ask—*those who are out "to get you."* It is possible that the only trouble with these people is that their egos are hungry because of your reluctance to feed them. This simple gesture on your part may be all that is necessary to get them on your side.

The first week of nightly preaching will be one of careful preparation for the big ingathering. Beginning with Sunday, the net must be drawn long and hard. Sunday alone should see at least one hundred people join your church. I have tried the following plan several times and have found it to work in every state in the South (except Virginia). Call all of your Sunday-school teachers together and make them pledge openly to support the meeting. Every teacher should pay a personal visit to every member of his class and exact a written promise from him to attend Sunday-school the coming Sunday. Cards can be printed for this purpose. All class members, saved and unsaved, should be encouraged to sign their names to these cards. This will be far more effective than getting their word, "I'll be there," or, "You count on me to attend." Have these signed cards returned to your office, where they will be sorted according to classes and departments. Put up a huge bulletin board on the platform in the church auditorium. Mount it in a conspicuous place and pin on the board those signed cards where everyone can see them each night during the first week of the revival. This will serve a very important purpose: it will put your Sunday-school teachers on the spot. It will also do the same to the members of the classes who sign those cards. Their signatures, pledging attendance at Sunday-school on the coming Sunday, will be in full view of everyone in the congregation!

When Sunday dawns, every detail of this plan should move like clockwork. Instead of letting the people go to their classes at the Sunday-school hour, arrange to have all of them above nine years of age assemble in the church auditorium. They will not know what is coming next, but you and the evangelist will! After two or three stirring gospel hymns, such as "Brighten the Corner Where You Are" and "Since Jesus Came into My Heart," present the evangelist and let him go to work. He should not preach longer than fifteen minutes—it's the invitation that is important.

During the invitation, which should last not less than thirty minutes, your best soul winners should be spotted in various sections of the auditorium where they can give personal encouragement to the unsaved to come forward. Sometimes a little shove toward the aisle is more effective than a dozen whispered words. So long as they keep coming down the aisles have the congregation continue the invitational singing. There is no better hymn for this period than "Jesus Is Tenderly Calling." (A second choice is "Why Do You Wait, Dear Brother?")

If there is a lull, and it seems that the more difficult ones have grown indifferent, stop the singing and request everyone to bow his head. While every head is bowed and all eyes are closed (except those of your trained soul winners), ask those who want to be prayed for to lift their hands. If they are hesitant, you can resort to a little pressure by saying something like this: "Unsaved man, unsaved woman, if you do not have the courage to come down the aisle now, surely you have the courage to lift your hand for prayer. The people are praying for you; the Lord will help you. No one is watching you but the pastor."

Your expert soul winners, who were previously instructed to spot those who requested prayer, will then go to work on those who lifted their hands. Continue the singing until you feel convinced that the Holy Spirit has finished His work for that service. As quickly as possible, begin the morning church service and repeat the above formula.

There are many other ways to "divert attention," but I am convinced that this one is the surest and most acceptable. It takes skill, planning, and work, but in the long run it will pay great dividends.

That the gospel may be preached in all the world, including the heathen lands, I am,

As always,

Astute

CHAPTER XV

Dear Charles:

In these past few letters you and I have been quibbling about what is and what is not a "church problem." In this letter I want to reverse most of what I have said and make a sweeping statement to the effect that there is only one real church problem as far as the lives of the people are concerned. That problem concerns the proper apportionment of recognition and power among the membership.

A wise administrator can handle this without too much difficulty. No matter how big a membership gets, there ought to be an office for every member. If you do not have enough offices to go around, create a few that the people never heard of. I know exactly what you are saying, "What are you going to do when some are important jobs and others are simply 'name' positions?" My answer to that is to institute the "rotating system" as quickly and as thoroughly as possible. This will distribute the important positions more equitably.

I must not mislead you here. There will be tremendous opposition to this suggestion. The people who have held important offices are not going to relinquish those offices without a struggle. But in this case you already have an overwhelming majority on your side. There are many times more on the "outside" than there are on the "inside"; thus if necessary you can bring the matter before the entire congregation and let them vote on it. There is absolutely no doubt how they would vote! I have tried it.

Every organization within the membership should operate on this system: no person should be eligible to hold any office longer than three years, with a period of one-year inactivity before he is again eligible for that same office. This should especially apply to your executive body, deacons or otherwise.

I wonder if you see the implications in this as far as your own security is concerned? The only men I could never handle were those who had got themselves so completely entrenched with endless terms that they had more power than I had. They were in those strategic positions long before I arrived on the scene, and they gave me to understand that they would be there long after I left. But you can easily see what this means to you if such power-mad people are forced out at the end of a three-year period. Of course, they will be eligible to come back on the Board at the end of the year. But by that time you can do a great deal toward weakening their influence.

Do not get discouraged by this. It is all a part of human nature, which was supposed to have got regenerated but never did. Here at the seminary the same thing occurs every year. At the last commencement the program chairman placed Professor Saddle fourth from the president's right, when he should have been third. To make matters worse he put Professor Needle third in Saddle's position. Needle and Saddle have hardly been on speaking terms since Needle was chosen to preach the Convention sermon four years ago. So you can see the embarrassment that was caused by this blundering incident. At the faculty meeting following commencement Professor Saddle tendered his resignation, but of course it was not accepted. I am glad it was not accepted because Saddle is a strong man; at least he is on our side.

One more experience will show you how prevalent this is, and why you should not be discouraged about it in your church. The chairman of the committee for the preparation of the seminary Catalogue allowed the printer to get by with printing Professor Side's name in smaller type than that used for the names of the other faculty members. It was a stupid mistake, but I sometimes think that Goad (who was the chairman) did it purposefully. To make matters worse, he omitted one of Professor Side's degrees. Side had just received an LL.D from Oshkosh, and he exploded worse than Saddle did. In fact, he demanded of Goad a personal apology.

So you see, it is not simply confined to the churches; it is everywhere.

Prayerfully yours,

Astute

CHAPTER XVI

Dear Charles:

In this letter I want to make what may appear to you to be a very strange suggestion. Cultivate the friendship of one or more Roman Catholic priests. You are sound enough in the true faith that such associations will not hurt you in the least. Their fantastic theology, ecclesiology, and idolatry of course cannot be taken seriously. But, Charles, these men are sharp, and from them you can learn a great deal.

I had never known a priest personally until I became a member of the Rotary Club. Then I got acquainted with Father O'Moore, and my pragmatic education was begun. He possessed one of the most charming and devastating personalities with which I have ever come in contact. He had all the men, including myself, eating out of his hand. He knew everybody by name and could tell the most humorous stories I have ever heard. (Some of them would not do for the Ladies' Aid!)

From there on I began to cultivate the friendship of these men. If I have picked up any *practical* knowledge that is worth while, I honestly believe I owe it to Father O'Moore and his associates.

Let me give you one illustration, and this may help you in deciding certain public-relation policies. If the Catholic Church happens to be a minority group in a given community, notice how insistent the priests are in advancing "brotherhood" and "tolerance." You would think that if there existed a fragment of brotherhood in the whole world, or in history past or present, it was really due to the brotherhood spirit which has dominated the Catholic Church for centuries! In such communities committees are set up, and the local priest will even agree to appear on the same platform with a Lutheran preacher and a Jewish rabbi.

Notice what happens, though, when the Catholic Church is overwhelmingly the dominant majority in a community. Do they scream for brotherhood? Do they form committees for the promotion of "tolerance"? The answer is obvious. Now our denomination is frequently in the very same position. You get the point: there is no earthly reason for going out on a limb when it is not necessary or when it is not to your advantage.

Then again, consider the tremendous hold the Roman Church has on its members. How we could learn from them in this regard! Professor Saddle was in South America several years ago, and while touring one of the capital cities he visited a large cathedral, a world-famous shrine. There he bought for five dollars a small box which he was told contained a piece of wood from the cross of Christ. He was further assured that carrying this box with him would keep him safe from a violent death for a period of one year. The superstition repulses you (as it did me) but, my boy, consider the grip they have on their people compared with what we have.

Not too long ago, out on the west coast of our own country, a priest and his lady companion were arrested for being drunk in public. One small newspaper dared publish this incident. The bishop in that particular diocese immediately threatened to boycott any other paper that dared publish the details of this incident. Further publicity to this juicy story was killed as far as our powerful American press was concerned. Though I cautioned you against reading the *Christian Unlimited Magazine,* I am indebted to the editors for this information. It appeared in the issue of December 13, 1944, page 1442. What does this reveal? It simply means that the priests have developed a very effective way of preventing the Church from being embarrassed in the eyes of the public. And this is as it should be. I am quite sure that the priest involved was severely punished, possibly defrocked, but the Church was saved. And this is just as important to our denomination as it is to the Catholic Church.

Consider Hollywood. I grow exceedingly impatient with many of our men who sit back and lament the tragic story of how the Catholic Church has invaded the Jewish-financed movie industry. Instead of criticizing Catholic leaders for this amazing stroke of strategy, I have nothing but admiration for them. They saw an opportunity for advancing their cause, and immediately set to work to accomplish their desired purposes. That they have succeeded is indisputable. Even the Protestant clergy has benefited to a certain extent, for the Protestant preacher is no longer consistently depicted as a country moron. I know, in one or two instances, that the preacher has appeared in a kindly light.

However, the thing that impresses me at this writing is when the theme of a great picture concerns a Catholic priest. When this crooner-character is shown on the screen, there is created a quiet, reverent hush as if Jesus Christ himself had made his appearance.

I suggest that for your devotional reading today you turn to Luke 16:1–9.

Tolerantly yours,

Astute

NOTE TO READER: After carefully reading this practical suggestion from Professor Astute, I could not help wondering how the old man would have reacted to the dramatic Vatican decree banning all priests, including good American citizens like Father O'Moore, from membership in Rotary.

W. S.

CHAPTER XVII

Dear Charles:

I am terribly depressed today. There are days when I feel as if I could not pull through, and this is one of them. My age is against me, but I have been tired a long, long time. Exhaustion and fatigue plague me every day, and when night comes I get no rest. Weak sedatives are of very little help. There are nights when I do not close my eyes.

Word has come that Vivian, my daughter, is in more trouble. Another fracas in a Brooklyn night club. Many times I have said that I would rather see her dead than as she is. Suffering of some kind is to be expected in this world, but I sometimes wonder why there is so much and why it lasts so long. The good, it seems, suffer more than the wicked.

Writing to you always picks me up, so I turn to this as a relief for my dejected mood. In my last letter I mentioned that there are certain associates whose friendship you should cultivate. Now I suggest that there are several more of the same nature.

Charles, you and I are a part of a great denomination. It is bigger and more important than either of us. It deserves our utmost loyalty, and first place in our hearts and affections. Nothing must ever come between you and the denomination. There is a patriotic expression, "Our country, right or wrong," which can be applied to the way you should feel toward the denomination. Do you understand me when I say that nothing in God's world should be placed ahead of your denomination? It is the denomination that demands your strength and talents. Remember always! The denomination is first, above and beyond anything in the entire universe.

There will be times when your loyalty will be severely tested. On such occasions I shall be praying that you will come through with flying colors. We have in our denomination a growing number of younger men whom I call "ecumaniacs." These men have been misled by the most vicious type of religious propaganda. This propaganda attempts to make differences appear identical, and this cannot be done. There is no doubt about it: there is no place for union or blind cooperation with the other so-called churches. In answer to your question about joining the Interdenominational Pastor's Conference, I suggest that you refrain. You have all you can do to make your denominational Pastor's Conference effective. Besides, you do not see any of the Catholic priests wasting their time around such meetings, do you?

We must face realities. Pray tell me, what do we have in common with the Presbyterians, who sprinkle infants, and Methodists, who not only sprinkle infants but who violate the Scriptures at every turn, especially in the manner in which they place their pastors? These men are moved around like checkers on a board. How in this world can the Holy Spirit operate under that kind of system? In such a holy matter nothing should interfere with the Spirit, but I am afraid our Methodist friends do not know this. The same applies to all the other denominations. So do not permit any of the "ecumaniacs" to influence you.

Cooperating with denominational leaders has other advantages. To make clear what I mean, I must refer to an incident that occurred during my first pastorate. Though I was young and inexperienced, I was given an important place on the State Board. It did not take me long to see that some of the employed state secretaries were not doing their job well, and I sought for an appropriate way to call this to the attention of the Board. Finally, at a closed meeting, I suggested that the Board call these men before the group in order that they might give an account of their stewardship.

Within a week I received a personal letter from each of the gentlemen involved thanking me for making this timely suggestion to the Board. A month later came another closed meeting with these men present. The chairman invited each to state his case, and, so help me, here is the approach each used: "Brethren, this is one of the highlights of my ministry. You men realize the work which you have given me is heavy and the burdens are many. I interpret my being here tonight as the greatest sign of encouragement of my ministry. I am indebted to each of you for giving me this opportunity to share with you the various phases of the responsibility which you have asked me to assume. The first one of these problems is the lack of an adequate staff. I need at least three additional assistants immediately," and so on.

As each of these men talked I knew I was done for. I realized for the first time that I was no match for such masters of political intrigue; I was a babe in the woods. These experienced leaders knew, however, that though they had swayed the entire Board with a description of their heavy burdens, they had had a close call.

They never forgot, nor did they ever forgive me. When the time came that I was forced to resign my pulpit, with a wife and child and no place to go, they saw to it, through their many church connections, that not a single door would open to me.

I had committed the unforgivable sin.

Fraternally yours,

Astute

P.S. Your decision not to have anything directly to do with the women's work and the choir reveals your good sense and also that you are learning fast.

CHAPTER XVIII

Dear Charles:

Just as there are friends to cultivate, there are others to be avoided. It is not necessary that you hate those in this latter group; however, it is absolutely essential that you do not get classified as one of them. This could happen very easily, because these dangerous men are in our own denomination, and their number grows larger with every passing year. At first they were pastors of small churches without power or influence. Now they are everywhere, even in some of the most outstanding pulpits in our region. Though there is always a close investigation of such matters, a few of these men have actually infiltrated into denominational positions. Right now this condition is giving me more concern than anything else.

My concern is deepened because I know where these men are coming from—they are coming straight from the classes of Professors Needle and Goad right here on our own campus! These younger men do not get such ideas of themselves; they are powerfully influenced by sinister personalities, who in this case happen to be my colleagues.

The first group are those who are "worship mad." Worship, worship, worship, worship, is all you hear. They have gone crazy on the subject, and of course they do not realize the implications. I have argued with Professors Needle and Goad until I am blue in the face that the course Worship and Evangelism should be changed to Worship *or* Evangelism. I am now convinced the two are irreconcilable and I warn you, if the "worship bug" ever bites you your evangelistic ministry is ended.

There are *seven* important steps toward killing the evangelistic spirit. Study them carefully and see how much damage has already been done in your own church. The first sounds very trivial, but it is the entering wedge—a heavy carpet on the floor. This has a tendency to produce quietness, but also to create a more formal atmosphere. Second, injecting periods of "meditation" and organ music in the order of service. Third, the wrong choice of hymns. When your congregation begins to sing such hymns as "Where Cross the Crowded Ways" and "A Loftier Race There'll Be," the fires of evangelism begin to lose their glow. Not only are these hymns antagonistic to what we are after, but the choir gets the notion that "Amen" has to be sung after each one of them. The right atmosphere can be produced only by singing such hymns as "Stepping in the Light," "Brighten the Corner Where You Are," "Throw Out the Life-Line," "Draw Me Nearer," "Beulah Land," and so on. Fourth, the introduction of "responsive readings." When a good hymn has created the right mood, it can be dissipated by having the people jump up and repeat like parrots, a responsive reading. Fifth, a robed choir. You can reduce your additions by fifty a year simply by permitting your choir to appear robed at all the services. Sixth, remodel the auditorium. Call the auditorium "sanctuary"; eliminate the pulpit platform and convert it into a "chancel." Imagine a chancel in a church of our faith! I heard of one of our churches doing this very thing several years ago. They made a chancel and divided the choir so that the choirs face each other rather than the congregation. Some of the members of this particular congregation insisted on putting the pulpit stand on the side of the chancel rather than in the center! Fortunately, there were a sufficient number of sensible people left to defeat this Episcopal arrangement. In our tradition the preacher has always been at the center of the service; it will be a sad day when he is shifted to some lesser place. Seventh, don the pulpit gown. This is the last step before decay and death. Charles, if you have ever had any such foolish ideas, I hope you will get them out of your head, once for all.

I now want to say a word about giving the invitation. Unless you have been influenced in the wrong direction, you already know the truth in what I am about to say. I have watched you closely on such occasions and have admired the masterful way you close a meeting. The little suggestion that I now make helps to retain the continuity of the service. There are four appealing invitational hymns that ought to be used to close every service, rotating each of them, of course, through the month. These are "It's No Secret," "Only Trust Him," "Take the Name of Jesus With You," and "Jesus Paid It All." When you have given your final illustration, and warmly extended the invitation, do not permit the organist to play a lengthy prelude. This has a tendency to destroy the effect which you have created throughout the entire service. Instead of the lengthy prelude, have the organist give only the opening chord; train your choir to rise and to begin singing immediately. With a slight wave of your arms you can have the congregation on their feet; lost people will be coming down the aisles before they have time to grow cold.

In your past several letters you have gone out of your way to tell me that your church had 240 additions last year. In case you should begin to feel too good about this, I want to remind you that it is only east of the Mississippi where more than 150 additions are considered phenomenal; west of the Mississippi, as is your case, anything less than 250 additions is considered mediocre.

I want to remind you also that it is a good thing not only to have a large number of additions but also to have, each year, a dozen or more young people commit themselves to full-time Christian service. This is the only way your church can really justify its existence, and it is the only way our denomination can remain alive. If you should say that such matters should be left entirely to the young people and the Lord, I would reply, and not sacrilegiously, that there are some matters where the Lord can do a better job if he has a lot of help. No, it is your sacred duty, not only to preach life-commitment sermons, but to single out these young people individually and put the pressure on them.

Sympathetically yours,

Astute

CHAPTER XIX

Dear Charles:

The next group of preachers to avoid is that which is constantly attempting to mix business and religion or, worse still, politics with religion. When you examine the situation closely, you will discover how silly it is for a preacher to be telling a businessman how to operate his business. I know such preachers counter this criticism by saying that they are not attempting to tell businessmen how to operate their businesses, they are simply concerned with the "human factor," the human relations that exist in business. It is true that something ought to be done about the poisonous hate that exists between management and labor. But this is such a controversial issue, that I see nothing else for a sensible pastor to do but to keep hands off and let the two groups destroy each other. After all, our job is preaching the gospel.

As to politics and religion, this is like trying to mix alcohol with driving a car. The two cannot be done. They are poles apart, and there is no use trying to get them together.

You will be interested to know that Professors Needle and Goad will also be leaving the seminary faculty next year. I decided that before I was retired, I would do the seminary one last good turn. I got in touch with several influential members of the Board of Trustees and explained to them frankly where these uncooperative preachers were coming from. The matter is now settled; Needle and Goad are going and both the seminary and the denomination will be safe for a while, at least.

The thing that influenced my decision to go to the Board of Trustees was a chat that I had with one of the outstanding businessmen of our city, a leading director of our largest bank. He was indignant at the existing situation, having discovered his own pastor meddling in business and politics! This layman told me that, though he regretted it, he had already made up his mind to join the Episcopal Church. Now, Charles, we can ill afford to lose men like that. I can remember a day in the life of our denomination when men of that caliber could be numbered on the fingers of one hand. So there was nothing left for me to do except to go to the Board, and that I did.

May the Holy Spirit always direct you,

Astute

P.S. If you can remain patient a little while longer, I think I shall be in a position to give my full sanction to your getting a new Packard or Cadillac. At the moment, however, anything more than a Dodge would be considered bad taste.

CHAPTER XX

Dear Charles:

Some time ago I cautioned you against using slang. There are times, however, when slang more aptly describes a situation than does proper speech. There is no word in the English language more fitting than "screwballs" to describe the preachers in the last group that you are to avoid. To become identified with any of these would prove disastrous. I refer specifically to those who try to solve the race problem. Here is a situation that has existed for centuries, and there is not a thing in this world that we can do to change it. Anyway, this knotty problem is working out amicably in our own region; a thousand years from now things may be slightly different, but that will be somebody else's responsibility. Right now this race thing is dynamite, and I suggest that you preach the gospel and avoid even the slightest reference to it. Whatever the New Testament means when it talks about breaking down that middle wall of partition between Jew and Greek, between bond and free, male and female, you and I know that it does not mean that a white man should ever eat across the table from a black man, even though both of them may be Christians.

I was very much upset by a story that came out of Georgia several years ago. One of my own students began to violate the great traditions of our region. What it is that possesses a man on such occasions I am at a loss to understand. In this young fellow's case, he had a strong church, a lovely wife, and a promising future. But he threw it all away over a question for which there is no answer. I have strongly suspected that such men have motives with which we are not familiar. In this case I am positive that there was a motive that never came to light. He was outspoken and stubborn, until at last in desperation his church asked for his resignation. He was actually driven out of his home state. This disturbed me for two reasons: first, Georgia sends more ministerial students to our seminary than most states; and we cannot afford a decrease in enrollment; second, the newspapers were full of the sorry story and the position of the denomination was greatly jeopardized in that area.

If you will look for them, there are compensations for everything, and this incident is no exception. I got some comfort out of knowing that my former student made the local editor of a prominent newspaper appear to be the jackass he is. And he did it without attempting a reply! A few months before the incident occurred, this crusading editor had run a series of articles on the subject "The Failure of the Church in Our Time." In one of his bitterest editorials he scorched all preachers for being cowards (he even called them "prostitutes"). "We need a revival of old-time religion," he said, "and this cannot be accomplished without a courageous clergy. In the olden days men preached the gospel without fear of devils or men. Today many of our preachers are nothing more than prostitutes and stooges for powerful men who pay the church bills, including the preachers' salaries." It was this same editor and paper that helped crucify my former student for his courageous stand on the race issue.

One final word as I come toward the close of this series of letters. A few years ago pulpit committees were composed of the most ignorant men I have ever encountered. Most of them were successful in their own businesses, but what they did not know about calling a preacher would fill a book. Committees from the larger churches were interested in "liberal" men. If it were not so tragic it would be positively humorous to discover what these laymen meant when they went looking for a "liberal" preacher. They simply wanted a pastor who would be tolerant of their pet vices, one who would overlook such things as their taking a cocktail and attending the races. In calling these "liberal" men, church leaders have had to learn the hard way. They sometimes got stuck with something so hot that, though they soon wanted to turn loose, it was impossible to do so. The churches were often humiliated by the independent and dogmatic stand taken by these "liberal" preachers on the most controversial issues of our day!

Not being informed about such matters, the committees knew only two things to do: they checked the statistics of the preacher's present pastorate, and they bargained with the candidate in an attempt to get him "for as little as he will accept."

That situation has remarkably changed within the past few years. Now many of these pulpit committees shoot direct questions at a prospective pastor: "Dr. Prince, will you cooperate 100 per cent with the leaders of our great denomination?" "Dr. Prince, can we depend on you to preach the gospel and say nothing pertaining to business or politics?" "Dr. Prince, will you accept, without question, the customs of our community regarding the matter of race relations?"

Charles, you must be in a position to answer these questions correctly, not simply by word of mouth, but by your record.

For Jesus' sake,

Astute

P.S. In my last letter I told you that I had reported Professors Needle and Goad to the Board of Trustees. These men cannot be trusted. For one thing they put Christianity above the denomination and they are always talking about "brotherhood" as if they meant it. So it gives me considerable satisfaction to know that when I am forced to leave the seminary in May, certain other individuals will also be leaving.

CHAPTER XXI

Dear Charles:

In spite of all my efforts to the contrary, I can tell by the undertones in your last letter that you have been somewhat influenced by one of our deadliest foes. "The Federal Council may not be as bad as our leaders seem to think," you say. I hope you have not been foolish enough to voice such an opinion to anyone but me. Your entire future, in our great denomination, can be terminated before you have time to realize what happened to you. It is not necessary to serve on a Federal Council committee or speak on one of its missions; all you have to do in our region is to voice openly such naïve sentiments as the one above and you will know what sudden denominational death is.

Personally, I believe the Federal Council of the Churches of Christ in America is the literal incarnation of Satan. Too long we have made our children think of Satan with horns and a pitchfork, when all the time his infernal majesty is the devilish Federal Council. I can think of no greater threat to our denominational solidarity than this hideous system which proposes to bring the Protestant groups closer together. We are out not only to conquer the South and the Nation but *the whole world*—and we must do it in the name of the denomination which we represent. The plain question to face is, "How can we achieve our sole objective if we get mixed up in any entangling alliances?"

No, Charles, we are committed to the destruction of the Federal Council by one means or another. Fortunately, we now have a lot of support. (There was a time, not too long ago, when we fought alone.) The Roman Catholic Church has, at last, seen the same threat which we have faced, and their leaders are prepared to do something about it. Their plan is to discredit the Federal Council on the grounds that it is Communistic. Don't laugh at this strategy—to be sure the Federal Council is controlled by a group of Episcopal vestrymen and Presbyterian elders, and it may seem absurd to think that the masses of people would go for the Communist angle when applied to such businessmen, but Catholic leaders in this country are shrewd—they know a good thing when they see it. Thus you can expect to see them ride this horse for some time to come. What else can they do? The Federal Council has prevented the Roman Catholic invasion of tax funds for parochial schools in various parts of the country. Of course, we too are opposed to the Catholic use of tax money—but you can't play both sides. It's either the Federal Council or Roman Catholics. Since we are not yet bothered with too many Catholics in the South, I'll take the Catholics.

The second group of allies upon whom we can depend are those industrialists who have made the "profit motive" synonymous with Christianity. At various times the Federal Council has dared to flout these gentlemen with strong economic pronouncements. The Council more than once has suggested that uninhibited capitalism would have to submit to certain controls or else bring economic disaster to the nation and the world. These industrialists have labeled such pronouncements "socialism," and I think the term is an accurate one. But, of course, there is no point in going further into the confusing situation, because we are all socialists—it is just a matter of degree. The conservative farmer is the most "socialized" creature in America, and his socialization has meant the prosperity which we have known for some time. Nevertheless, straightening out these complexities is not our job—we can sit back and thank God for these powerful men who hate the Federal Council as much as we do.

The third group of allies is that of the ultra-conservatives in all Protestant denominations. The Federal Council has left itself wide open; the charge here is Bible heresy. Some of the preachers (and laymen) connected with the Council have written books and pamphlets and have made certain statements which indicate that they do not believe the Bible to be the literally inspired and infallible Word of God. One scholar wanted to know which Bible manuscript was verbally inspired—since there are scores of them. Another indicated that God did not send bears to eat up the little children who called the prophet Elisha "baldheaded." His position was that the writer of that portion of Scripture simply *thought* that God sent those bears. You see, Charles, the danger of putting a thing down on paper? This Bible-heresy angle is almost as good as Communism.

So, the Federal Council is no longer a real threat to our individual security. However, it is to our advantage to keep the people thinking that it is. Instead of your considering, "The Federal Council may not be as bad as our leaders seem to think," you should keep before your members the ever present danger of this evil system.

By the way, there is a practical use that can be made

of the Federal Council issue. At our great annual conventions, there is usually introduced some motion or resolution which does not exactly fit in with our tradition. (Watch the Social Service Committee here.) At the right moment, during the debate, get the floor, raise your voice to an emotional pitch, and somewhere in the midst of your condemnation of the motion shout the words "Federal Council of the Churches." Repeat this a couple of times, and before you know it you can stampede ten thousand people and kill any proposition with which you are in disagreement. I have seen it done more than once, and often envied the men who had the nerve and ability to do it.

With all my love,

Astute

NOTE TO READER: Since Professor Astute wrote these words, the Federal Council of the Churches has become a part of the National Council of the Churches of Christ in America.

W. S.

CHAPTER XXII

Dear Charles:

As you undoubtedly know, for the past several years I have had a certain church in mind for you. It will give you not only power and prestige but an opportunity to demonstrate the unusual gifts with which you have been endowed. As yet, this pulpit has not "opened up." The present pastor is not in good health, so from this standpoint anything can happen within the next year or two. It is also generally known that he is in serious difficulty with his official board. He was undiplomatic in his insistence on rotating members of the board every three years. As I have warned you repeatedly, things of this nature must be handled with kid gloves. One of two things then will happen in this church in the not too distant future: either the Lord will call the pastor home to glory or his board will ask for his resignation. At any rate, I am confident you will someday be the shepherd of this tremendous flock. The Holy Spirit moves in mysterious ways. It has been my policy to wait upon Him in all things pertaining to the work of the Kingdom. This matter is no exception. We shall wait upon Him until something happens. In the meantime, however, I have several friends in this particular congregation who are spreading the word around quietly that *you* are their man.

The church staff you now have, though large, is entirely inadequate. Things will be different in the next situation. Of course, you will be in complete charge. There can be no such thing as "dual authority." You can count on at least the following assistants to aid you in putting across your vast program: associate pastor, assistant pastor, assistant to the pastor, pastor's assistant, church secretary, financial secretary, records secretary, private secretary, minister of music, minister of education, assistant minister of education, Department No. 1; assistant minister of education, Department No. 2; assistant minister of education, Department No. 3; assistant minister of education, Department No. 4. Thus it can be seen that you will have a full, well rounded staff. There will be some headaches connected with keeping all these people happy and cooperative, but with your charm and winsome personality I have no fears on this point.

There is one additional staff member which you must request the board to secure immediately upon your becoming pastor of this great church. At the present time this person is not usually included on a church staff. But I am convinced that within the next twenty-five years every large city church will employ such a person. He will be a combination public-relations man and publicity agent. There may be some doubt about certain staff members, mentioned above, earning their salaries, but there will be no such question about a good, capable publicity agent.

Where did I learn this? You know my admiration for a certain cardinal in a large metropolitan area. The power this man possesses makes my head dizzy. His constituents bow and scrape before him. Their eternal destiny is in his hands. In various ways they are gently reminded of this momentous fact. The power he wields over secular institutions in his area fascinates me. Being pushed around all my life, I suppose, makes me crave just a little taste of this for myself . . . if not for myself, then for you, Charles. But it is not simply the "power" he possesses that is so impressive; it is the interpretation of this man's personality, held by the people in his area, that intrigues me. What is that interpretation? A man meek and mild, as meek and mild as the lowly Jesus! Years ago I learned that the cardinal employs a highly paid press agent. This man has proved to be worth his weight in gold. Every day of the year some kind of favorable notice concerning the cardinal appears in at least one of the great daily papers—his picture at least once a week. He makes a speech, grants an audience to a presidential candidate, blesses a new building, and so on. There is no limit to what a good press agent can do under such circumstances! You may wonder if this does not violate the words and spirit of Jesus when he said, "Blessed are the *meek* for they shall inherit the earth." Do not let this upset you. These words, as you know, are from the Sermon on the Mount. Though I would not want my students to know it, I have long held the opinion—privately, of course—that the Sermon on the Mount is the most impractical nonsense I have ever read. A favorable press is an essential requirement to a successful career. Regardless of the Bible, or anything else, both the successful cardinal and the successful pastor must have the press on their side. By the way, the only time the "other nature" of this "meek" religious dignitary was exposed, even slightly, was when he lost his temper and denounced a certain lady whom some people hold to be great but whom I consider to be a clown. Charles, the cardinal did this without advice from his press agent. His public apology was immediately forthcoming. He swallowed his words and lost face, both for himself and for his Church. Rest assured, the cardinal will never make that mistake again! Charles, when you succeed in getting a press agent for a staff member, let this blunder of a high ecclesiastical official be a lesson to you. The rule is: If you hire a man to do a publicity job, let *him* do it. That is his business. He knows more about such matters in one day than you will know in a lifetime. To my knowledge, I have never given you better advice than this. Heed it, my boy, heed it.

In addition to being a public-relations man and a competent press agent, this staff member will know how to promote your own church program. Thus it will be necessary for him to be of our denomination. He must be thoroughly familiar with every plan, project, and program that is being launched and sponsored by every board, agency, and institution within the Convention. He should have a knack for applying secular techniques to church-related programs. There is no difference between selling insurance and selling religion. What works with one will work with the other. There is a "product" to be marketed, there are customers to be "sold." The "know-how" in meeting the customer, beating down stubborn resistance, getting the name on the dotted line applies to *insurance*; it also applies to *religion*. The professors here at the seminary are somewhat timid about this. They are still holding out for the long, tedious processes of education. My position is, get their names on the dotted line first, and then, if you are still interested in educating the converts, do that later.

Your additional staff member must also have the knack of writing catchy slogans. (Not everybody can do this.) The Kingdom of God will advance in direct proportion to the kind of slogan the masses of people are made to repeat. The truth in this principle can be confirmed by any good advertising man. Our denomination has an excellent chance to gain a monopoly on the religious world *in this generation.* A number of slogans come to my mind which I am sure would help our cause along. In 1944 I suggested the following to those in positions of higher authority, but they did not take warmly to it. Perhaps, at a future date, wiser leaders will reconsider. The slogan was "A Billion More in '44." Imagine the results we could have achieved if we had been successful in getting millions of our members to repeat that slogan every day during the year! In 1948 I suggested—again to no avail—"Don't Trust to Fate in '48." At present there is a note of expectancy, perhaps desperation, in the air. Quietly, I am insisting to our leaders that come 1952, we adopt as our Convention-wide slogan, "Our Dreams Will Come True in '52." It pleases me to tell you that my latest suggestion is receiving prayerful attention from those who previously paid little attention to what I had to say.

Regardless of what the denomination does about this "slogan strategy," I strongly recommend it when you take over the responsibilities of your new position. The staff member I suggested—public-relations man, publicity agent —will prove himself invaluable.

Waiting for the Holy Spirit to move in His good time, I am,

As always,

Astute

P.S. Charles, if we are going to take the world for our denomination, one other matter must be frankly faced. It is up to you and all others in positions of influence and power to enforce among your members an indispensable regulation. *All forms of birth control must go.* The use of contraceptives for any purpose or under any circumstances must be interpreted not simply as "sinful" but as "criminal." On the subject of how to make this mandatory, I have no suggestions. The "how" is your problem. I can only say that rigid enforcement must be accomplished by one method or another or we stand a chance not simply of losing the foreign lands but of losing the good old U.S.A.

CHAPTER XXIII

Dear Charles:

It is inconceivable that one could write as many things as I have written to you without contradicting himself at one place or another. However, do not jump to conclusions in this matter. What I have said in this fashion may only be an "apparent contradiction." With this word of caution in mind, please read the present letter slowly, digesting every word.

You know how I have always warned you about trying to mix religion with politics. It simply cannot be done. Besides, if you should try, it will be disastrous as far as your future is concerned. In this day and time most of your deacons care very little what you believe about the Virgin Birth. After all, a person's life is affected only slightly by the acceptance or rejection of this doctrine. On the other hand, the way you feel about "enterprise" is of paramount importance. I suggest you take time to find out how the great leaders of the land interpret "enterprise." Begin with the Chamber of Commerce, then the National Association of Manufacturers, then the American Medical Association. (Of course, if you were in another type of situation, I would refer you to the C.I.O. and the A.F. of L.)

After you have found out what their position is you can do two things. First, spread the word around softly in your personal contacts that you are in *full* agreement. You have unlimited invitations to speak before groups such as the Women's Club, Junior League, Rotary, Kiwanis, Lions, Elks, Moose, Exchange, and so on. Don't use the direct approach. Choose a topic such as "Building Character." With such a topic you may have a number of subpoints: "Good character is molded by competition"; "Good character means success"; "Good character gets results"; "Good character is 100 per cent Americanism." Second, from the pulpit you must be even more subtle. The purpose of getting this viewpoint into a sermon is not to explain anything. (Let the politicians and economists do that.) Rather, it is to let your church officials know where you stand on the points which they now cherish more highly than religious doctrines. Sometimes this can be done with an amusing story. At other times it can be done with an innocent, passing reference to an experience you had with "an outstanding executive of a noted steel corporation." In this way you have not preached a "political sermon," yet you have let everyone know where you stand.

Since I began writing these letters to you, a notable shift has occurred in the thinking of the people. It is obvious that there must be a change in the national administration. Take it easy here. Find out which way the wind is blowing in your state and then make your decision. Because of our political tradition, I realize that in the South we are on somewhat of a spot. However, I have learned that for his own good there are times when a man must change his mind. This is one of those times.

A change in administration must be brought about for four reasons. First, once and for all the mess in Washington will be cleaned up. Harmony will prevail and everyone will feel that he is a part of one big team. Second, Communists have taken over every important spot in the government, including the State Department, the Treasury Department, the Justice Department, and the Supreme Court. If it were not for a few faithful "watchdogs" in the Senate, the overthrow of the government, under the present administration, would already have been accomplished. This fact can be verified by reading the leading newspapers of the nation. Almost without exception they are agreed on this point. Charles, if a man cannot believe the great newspapers of this land, what can he believe?

Third, there must be a change so that the war with Communism can be terminated. The Korean War was started by our national leaders to divert attention from their mistakes. It is true that the Communists acted aggressively in invading South Korea and it is also true that in challenging them in Korea, further drives in Greece, Iran, and so on have thus far been interrupted. However, the present administration has proved itself without a foreign policy and completely inadequate to deal with world problems. What is needed is an administration that will bomb China and Russia off the map and put an end to Communism once for all.

Fourth, a change in administration is needed in order to reduce taxes. Various authorities have pointed out that we are fast approaching national bankruptcy. There was never a time in our history when the economy was threatened as it is now. We are spending ourselves into ruin. One of our senators, noted for his economy views, has pointed out how many millions could be saved if such things as farm price supports, the program of aid to the states in erecting hospitals, slum clearance, and milk for underprivileged school children could be eliminated. In considering this last suggestion there is only one thing that disturbs me. Though this particular senator did not indicate it, I recently saw some reliable statistics to the effect that if all the welfare agencies and bureaus were shut down there would be a saving of only 1½ per cent of the Federal budget. More than 80 per cent of our tax money appears to be going for military purposes, past and present.

However, top leaders in the opposition have insisted that taxes can and will be reduced at least 30 per cent the *first* year after there is a change in administration. This thing of taxes touches us all in a vital spot. I see nothing to lose and everything to gain by supporting the trend for a change.

Study these things carefully. There must be no slip-ups here. Remember, no "political sermons." Just enough to let your officials know that you are with them down the line.

Yours for a change,

Astute

P.S. This blasting of China and Russia with bombs may sound a little harsh to you, but I am now convinced that Communism cannot be wiped out in any other way and neither can peace be achieved. You cannot negotiate with that which is non-negotiable. But bombs can do for Communism what they did for Hitlerism, which is now dead and forgotten. My authority for this opinion is none other than the greatest military leader in the history of mankind, a man who would have ended the Korean conflict long ago if they had given him a free hand.

CHAPTER XXIV

Dear Charles:

It now looks as if I shall be forced to make a trip to New York. My cross grows heavier every year. Some people say that though they would not enjoy living in New York, a visit there is a wonderful privilege. Personally, I dread even the thought of a visit. The smell of sin is in the air. The people are wicked, lustful, and immoral. I feel contaminated when I visit the place even for a short while. But some things in this life you must force yourself to do, and for me this trip appears to be one of them.

Before taking off I shall write a brief and hurried reply to your recent query, "How to justify proselytizing members from other congregations." The answer to this question falls into two natural categories. First, getting members from churches within our own denomination, and second, getting members to join from other denominations.

Concerning the first, this can be said about your own situation. You have much that is superior to offer people in your city. Your building, though not beautiful, is large and adequate. Thousands of dollars have been expended to provide efficient facilities. Your Sunday-school annex can take care of one thousand people. This gives you an advantage over the churches which are crowded for space. In addition, you have a superior program. You have such things as teacher and officer promotional meetings, special days for community-wide visitation, and regular evangelistic revivals. Under such circumstances I see no reason why your conscience should hurt you if you should succeed in persuading a family from another church of our own denomination to join your church. You are simply offering them something better. Where is the harm in this?

Concerning the enlistment of members from other denominations, keep this in mind: the field here is wide open, hunting is good, and there are no restrictions. If you don't get their people, they will get yours. It's a matter of who gets there first with the most pressure. However, getting people to join from other denominations can be justified along other lines. Take, for instance, the matter of truth. There are not several kinds of truth. There is only Truth, with a capital "T." Never let this out of your mind for a moment: our denomination has the Truth. As an example: Presbyterians do not believe in the absolute autonomy of the local church. They also practice baptizing babies. Both of these are wrong. Can there possibly be any compromise with error? If you possess the Truth (as we do), you have the obligation to uphold it without reservation or deviation. Thus, with this thought firmly established, you can go forth to win the world in the name of our blessed denomination.

It is beyond me why you allow such thoughts to worry you even for one minute. This entire approach is sustained and reinforced by the society of which we are a part. It is rooted in our tradition and accepted in every walk of life without question. Why should there be any question when applied to religion and the church? Take, for instance, the relation of General Motors to Studebaker. Can you imagine the representatives of General Motors suffering any qualms over taking customers away from Studebaker? Of course the thought of such suffering of conscience is humorous. If General Motors could do so, they would make *every* Studebaker customer a General Motors customer. In the process they would drive Studebaker to financial bankruptcy and a few people might get hurt in the scramble. But, honestly, Charles, can you see anything wrong with such a procedure? That is business. And what is good business for General Motors is good business for the church.

You have enough problems without creating one out of your imagination. Settle down, go to work in earnest, and may your largest number of additions be recorded in this year's Convention annual.

Pray for me while I am away.

Defending the faith once for all delivered to the saints, I am,

As always,

Astute

CHAPTER XXV

Dear Charles:

No matter how old one grows, he should never cease to learn.

Recently I spent a month in New York City. Vivian broke over the traces again, and I made the trip in an effort to straighten her out. That I failed miserably is an understatement, but that is all I shall say about this unpleasant matter for the present.

While in New York I attended services in a church of a denomination other than our own. New York preachers are notorious for their heretical views; they are forever talking about such things as "racial equality," "economic justice," and so on. Not being sound in the faith, they cannot keep their feet on the ground. The first Sunday I attended church, I received the shock of my life. The place was packed and hundreds of people were turned away! If I had not arrived at the church a full hour early, I would not have secured a seat. I was so impressed by what I saw that I visited the same church for four consecutive Sundays. Each time the crowds were bigger and more people were turned away.

In a previous letter I stressed the fact that three types of sermons are now in demand—of course, I was speaking from a Southern point of view—sermons on comfort, sermons that expound the Bible literally, sermons that are evangelistic. In New York I found a preacher getting a phenomenal response and resorting to none of these approaches. I hope I have aroused your curiosity sufficiently so that by now you are shouting, "What in the world was he preaching?"

Charles, he was preaching "Peace of Mind." Does that sound too simple? I can't describe the impact of this service in a letter. You must see it in action to believe it. Each Sunday the preacher delivered the same sermon. The only difference was that several new words were added to the melody and new illustrations were used. These illustrations were taken from the preacher's personal experiences and usually began something like this, "While I was in Cleveland, the owner of a great department store asked me, 'Do you know how I use prayer to increase my sales?' " Or, "I talked to an important industrialist the other day who was discouraged because of the trend of business, especially the stock market. He said in humility that he comes to our church for the 'quiet period.' During that period of absolute silence, he makes contact with the Holy Spirit and frequently it is revealed to him what stocks are going up and what stocks are going down."

These illustrations were multiplied without number. You can imagine the response of the congregation. Religion, from this point of view, becomes the unashamed means toward a materialistic heaven. It is that kind of heaven for which our flesh cries. As you are well aware, I have never seen any good reason for refusing to give people what they want. This new approach really does it!

In addition to this economic twist (which I admit never before occurred to me), a great deal was said about overcoming an inferiority complex, conquering insomnia (one of my troubles), and relieving tension and anxiety. Using the illustration of a golfer whose ball went into the rough—grass eight inches high—the preacher insisted that one of the first rules of golf was to learn that the rough did not exist, except in the golfer's imagination. Once this principle is accepted, a man can conquer anything on the golf course or in life. Apparently, only religion can help him understand this. In fact, from this point of view, this is the dominant purpose of religion. This is my greatest discovery since Hadacol.

Speaking of Hadacol, I must confess that prior to my New York trip I had been drinking entirely too much of this tonic. But I needed it. My nerves are on edge; I worry constantly about Vivian and I am disturbed about the friction here at the seminary. Because the sedatives which I take for insomnia have ceased to help me, and Hadacol is rather expensive, I am going to give this "Peace of Mind" angle a personal try. But this must be made clear: whether or not it works on me is beside the point. The point is, this approach to religion is presently more in demand by the public than any other on the market, including "evangelism." When you are called to the important church I have in mind for you, I want you to give this message an honest trial.

I can hear you asking right now, "Will such an emphasis receive the same response in the South?" I am now confident that it will work anywhere, provided you develop the vocabulary and approach the matter in complete confidence. People in the South have just as many fears as other people. They share the same materialistic values and the same ambition for success. They have the same desire to escape from the unpleasantnesses of this world as New Yorkers do. As ministers of the gospel, I see nothing wrong in helping them achieve this goal.

Please, Charles, begin now to make a study of this novel approach to Christianity. I bought three books, all of them written by the preacher to whom I have referred, and under separate cover I am mailing them to you special delivery. My only twinge of conscience is that this man is not of our denomination. Perhaps in a situation like this a broader viewpoint is tolerable. At any rate, I want you to study these books carefully. Master the vocabulary and style, and when you are sure of yourself give "Peace of Mind" a fair trial.

The implications in putting this across successfully are exciting. If you can master this approach, do you realize that you can forget just about every technique I have taught you? Take, for example, the matter of house-to-house visitation which is in so much demand in the South. If you can sell "Peace of Mind," you no longer will have to beat the bushes for unwilling converts—they will come in droves to you!

With warm regards and assuring you that I have just poured my last bottle of Hadacol down the drain, I am,

Peacefully yours,

Astute

P.S. In the event (and this is a possibility) that you cannot master this approach, or that it does not get a sweeping response, you will of course have judgment enough to drop it immediately. The ideas on church promotion which I have shared with you in these letters are tested and tried, and it will be a long time before they are outmoded in the South. You can always return to them when the need arises.

CHAPTER XXVI

My dear, dear Charles:

The news has just arrived, and I am beside myself with joy! Mr. Ghoul, chairman of the Pulpit Committee, at the First Church, Mammonville, wired me that the congregation extended you a unanimous call. There was not a single dissenting vote.

When I received the telegram I went straight to my room, and there I did something that I have not done for years; I cried like a baby. I made no effort to control my emotions. Such moments come to few men in a lifetime; thus there was no point in repressing the way I felt. To be the pastor of the largest church in a city of more than 300,000 is an honor that angels would covet. At last you have your chance!

Since Miranda went home to glory ten years ago, I have been a lonely old man. As you know, Vivian has never been a real daughter to me. Innumerable times she has humiliated me, and still she continues to do many things that I disapprove of. Recently she divorced her husband, and already she is planning a second marriage. I have never met the man she is engaged to, but they say he is, of all things, a "supporting actor" on Broadway. I suppose it would not be so bad if he were the real thing, but imagine Vivian marrying a "supporting" actor. Sometimes I think the child hates the very ground I walk on. Truly, "An ungrateful child is worse than sharpness to the teeth."

But, Charles, you are my son; my son in the gospel, which really makes you dearer to me than if you were my son in the flesh. How I have watched everything you have done during these years! Would you think me foolish if I told you I have kept a scrapbook of clippings giving an account of all the major offices which you have held, and the special talks and addresses which you have delivered? The two-column write-up of your Convention sermon is one that I prize dearly.

When Vivian's recklessness distressed me, and when the coldness of the men here at the seminary was more than I could bear, my thoughts turned toward you and the magnificent service you are rendering our denomination. Invariably I received strength and comfort from such thoughts. In some way I know that I shall have a small share in the harvest which you are reaping. Did I not lead you to Christ? Was it not under my ministry that you surrendered to preach? The knowledge of this is worth more to me than all else in this world. There is no personal honor which gives me so much satisfaction, and there is no disappointment that I cannot stand when I consider the wonder and mystery of the Lord's will in leading you from nowhere to this great and influential church.

Charles, you are now forty-two years old. This is the most critical period in any man's ministry. Most churches today are weary with their ministers by the time they reach your present age. Certainly forty-five is the limit of modern tolerance. Handsome, energetic men in their thirties are in demand. However, during these next ten important years—if you follow carefully the suggestions which I have made—you will be more warmly loved by the people of your new church than you have ever been. The stinging things I have written in these letters you have taken without offense, and this, on your part, reveals a beautiful spirit. It is this spirit which is worth even more than your natural ability.

One final word, Charles: keep humble. Humility is the mark of a great man. Remember always that you are where you are because of the guidance and leadership of the Holy Spirit. In the midst of many discouragements and losses, my own humility has been to me a source of satisfaction.

Commencement will be two weeks from now. That means the time of my retirement has arrived. If it were not for the prospect of getting to visit with you within the next few months, I doubt that I could survive the experience. After all, I have given twenty-eight years of my life to this grand old institution, and I have come to love everything about it. But beyond retirement I have one thing to look forward to: my visit with you in your Christian home. If, in any way, I have had a slight share in preparing you for the greatest experience of your life, I am truly grateful.

Until I see you,

Your obedient servant in Christ,

Astute

P.S. Your present congregation will be heartbroken when you resign. Severing such ties is the most difficult task in any man's ministry. However, you must help the people to understand that you are being called to a larger service and that you need their prayers as you face the heaviest responsibility of your entire life.

P.P.S. "Peace of Mind" has not worked for me. But remember what I said concerning your giving it a fair trial. If you develop the vocabulary and the style, I am sure that people in Mammonville will eat it up.

* * * * *

It was the irony of life that Professor Astute did not realize his ambition to visit with Charles, his son in the gospel. The next time he saw Charles was at the funeral service, where he was simply another spectator. Priscilla, in her coldness, refused to allow the old man to have the slightest part in the service.

As Professor Astute passed the casket in which Charles's body had been lying in state in the big auditorium of the First Church, Mammonville, he rebelled as never before. He had said goodbye to Miranda with the greatest of patience and faith; they would meet again on that bright golden shore. He could have looked into the dead face of Vivian, his only child, without a wince of pain, yea, with a feeling of relief. But not so with Charles.

Never had Charles looked so distinguished, so confident, and so sure of himself as he did in the great gold-trimmed, silk-lined casket. The magnetic smile, which he had perfected across the years, now in death crinkled slightly about his full lips. Though his eyes were closed, he appeared any minute to be ready to raise himself from his new bondage and greet each mourner by name, with a lusty handshake and a resounding slap on the back.

Astute paused before the casket and with unashamed bitterness cursed God for His stupidity in taking from the earthly scene one who was in the prime of life, one who had reached the top and was ready to go places, one who could have meant so much to the life of *the* denomination in its struggle for supremacy in the religious world. "Why?" was the anguished cry of the old man. "Why, O God, why? How could You do it to him?"

Professor Astute never knew another day's happiness in this world. Two months later he died of a broken heart. Thus he joined Charles in that realm beyond, where together they would face the searching judgment of God, who as yet has never allowed Himself or His people to be used as means to worldly ends.